Healing

THE

BROKEN

BRAIN

By Elden M. Chalmers

Printed by
Remnant Publications

Healing the Broken Brain

Cover image Copyright© 1998
Photodisc, Inc.

This Edition Published 1998

ISBN 0-9669314-0-8

Acknowledgements

I express my heartfelt thanks and appreciation to a wide group of scientists, clinicians, educators, clergy and lay readers for their suggestions that have made this book more helpful to the groups they represent.

A special "thank you" is extended to Drs. George Akers, Jack Blanco, Leona Gulley and Sherry Skidmore for their careful reading of the manuscript and their valuable suggestions.

The most significant and deeply appreciative acknowledgement is to my wife, Esther Widmer Chalmers, for her dedicated help in all stages of the creation of this book, for her penetrating editorial and writing skills, and her wise critical judgments.

My grown children, educator Donna Steen and clinical therapist Verlin Chalmers who all through childhood reminded me of the significance the principles discussed in this book and for sharing with me now the benefits of their experience in the helping professions.

I wish to express my gratitude to the authors of publications that I have used for research data and illustrations: J.C. Eccles, R.B. Cattell, Wilder Penfield, J. Achterberg and G. Frank Lawlis, Joan Borysenko, Richard Restak, Daniel Goldman, William Sadler, and a host of others acknowledged in the references and endnotes.

Furthermore, this book would not have been possible were it not for the contributions made by my clients who shared their insights and personal experiences, and provided the stories that bring color and beauty to the thesis of this book.

Finally, tribute is given to my personal friend, Jesus Christ, who patiently and incessantly shared his personal thought and love throughout the creation of this book.

Contents

CHAPTER ONE

Introduction

We were about to descend upon Bakersfield, CA in our 23 ft. Tioga motor home. The sun was rising on our right, the morning was cool and invigorating. I had awakened about an hour before, and my mind was full of questions.

I was thinking about my graduate students, those doctoral students in my counseling and psychotherapy courses, and many less trained would-be counselors or people helpers. They had been eager to learn about the mind and emotions.

I thought of so many hurting people out there—frustrated parents dealing with conduct-disordered children and delinquent adolescents, the attention-deficit disordered, the anxious, the depressed, the obsessed, the compulsive, those plagued with panic disorders and phobias and a host of other problems.

As my graduate students researched the theoretical foundations of Freud, Skinner, Rogers, Maslow, Ellis, Perls, Carkhuff, and scores of others, they wondered. Did these have the answers they needed to help people work through their troubled lives?

As they stretched their minds to understand the structure of the brain, both chemical and physical—and to grasp any relationships between structure and function, they wondered. Could these provide any clues, any answers to people problems?

The power of genetics—the chemical codes at work in every cell of body and brain! Thinking, concerned people are full of questions. Are people stuck with the way they were born? Can we fix it with genetic engineering? Or do we give up on helping people change and fix the problems of the human race with "genetic cleansing"?

Or is nurturing more powerful than the genes? What about improving parenting skills, grand-scale educational programming, hypnosis, and brainwashing, restructuring the legal system, controlling the media? Are we locked up in our problems because of how and what we think?

Or are we what we eat? Would dietary reforms provide the answer?

Do the Vedic priests of the East have the answer? They have claimed for centuries that the mind can release substances in the body to bring peace to the mind.[1] Western neuroscientists are discovering that the mind does indeed release chemical substances that directly determine the wide variety of emotions experienced by all of us.

Does the Bible, studied for centuries and touching the lives of millions, provide any solid, practical answers for the troubled lives of people today? Many renowned scientists say 'yes'. Many say 'no'. I see no necessary conflict between good science and divine revelation—between good science and good religion.

Scientific research is ever discovering new wonders. But good science reveals nothing that conflicts with the Bible rightly understood. In fact, I have found that often good science has shed light upon Bible pas-

2

sages, and Bible passages have shed light upon science. If we study with open minds, both science and the Bible will teach us something of the laws I believe God has established and through which He works!

My patients have found peace and freedom from their anxieties as they have developed a fellowship with this God "in whom" the Bible says "we live and move and have our being."[2] When Socrates, the wise man of Grecian culture shared with the Greek scholars the phrase "as a man thinketh, so is he", he was but echoing the words of the wisest man of all time, King Solomon, recorded in the Bible seven hundred years earlier.[3]

Today, neuroscientists are affirming that our thinking is so powerful that it can burst millions of chemical sacs to pour out chemicals at specific addresses in the brain and profoundly affect our moods, our emotions, and our actions. Beyond this, current findings disclosed by neuroscientist John Eccles and others show how our thinking can even modify our genes![4] Those Bible words "As a man thinketh, so is he" take on new and profound meaning with such research!

I thought once again of the vast multitude of hurting people out there—countless numbers, many who have never gone to a professional for help. Some were afraid to go. Some didn't know to whom they should go.

Could I help these kinds of people to recognize the highway to true healing for a broken brain? Could I inspire people to travel that highway? This book is an attempt to do that.

And then I thought of my own work in therapy and counseling—as a licensed psychologist for more than thirty years, and as a licensed and ordained minister

3

for twenty additional years before that. How do I do counseling and psychotherapy?

How do I sort through my memory bank during the counseling or therapy session? What leads me to choose some materials and reject others? How do I decide if a particular theoretical premise or strategic technique is the one to use?

What principles do I operate by? What fundamental truths, laws, or doctrines do I see operating in the thinking, feeling, and behavior of my clients caught in their problem webs? What propositions do I believe to be axiomatic or essential prerequisites to mental health and healing?

Could I communicate these principles and postulates to all that are interested in maximizing the healthy functioning of the brain?

As I thought of my clients, I thought of some that I had failed to help. I re-examined the possible reasons. I re-examined my own frustrations, and the times I failed to motivate. I recalled my pre-mature and ill-timed eagerness to usher a patient into a brand new world of peace, calm, and sanity. I remembered how easy it was to be insensitive to what people are really experiencing, how easy to focus on the wrong issues, or apply the wrong remedies.

I thought of hundreds of my clients that *had* found peace of mind and joy in living—freedom from the anxieties, the panic disorders, the depressions, the compulsions, the obsessions, the personality disorders, the conduct disorders, the post-traumatic stress disorders, the sexual disorders, and a host of other disturbing disorders. I wondered why so many of them never suffered a relapse and others did.

I thought of my apathetic students, my struggling students, and my failing students —those who left their failing grades behind them and climbed to the top of their classes. I thought of those once frustrated parents who beamed with joy and pride over their children's scholastic achievements.

I thought of children and adolescents who suddenly discovered that they were abusing a miraculous mind, an unbelievably powerful brain, —young people who then changed their life direction and winged their way to dramatic achievements.

While exceedingly grateful for the explosive and exponential increase of knowledge and *measurable* experience in both the *scientific* and *spiritual* realms, we recognize that we still need additional clear, well-defined answers to many aspects of the broken brain. Broken physically and psychologically.

In this search for answers, we can hear many voices calling us in different directions. To recognize the correct route on our journey to restoration and wholeness is challenging, to say the least. Accordingly, we have set out established principles and tested postulates along the way, like signposts, if you please.

We have included very few detailed maps, lest the guide or traveler grow weary trying to decide between the more scenic, the shortest, the fastest, or the most comfortable route! Everybody can choose.

There *are* sure and safe routes to healing. There are uncertain and dangerous routes. Tragically, many well-meaning people have chosen such dangerous paths that they have ended up worse off than when they started their journey.

The principles and postulates set forth in the following pages are well established and thoroughly tested. They are based on good science—findings that have been replicated by independent scientists, and upon Bible passages whose messages are repeated by several different Bible writers to be sure we are correct in our understanding.[5] When followed, thousands have found that these principles and postulates safely and surely lead to psychological health and wholeness.

In this book we are defining *a principle* as *a fundamental truth, a primary law, a basic law, or a governing law of conduct.* We are defining *a postulate* as **an axiomatic proposition, an underlying hypothesis that is an essential prerequisite to specific outcomes.**

It is my hope that the principles and postulates set forth in this book will be as guiding stars and the un-failing sun to keep all of us right on course, though sometimes over stormy oceans, to arrive safely into the haven of peace—peace of mind and soul. And in the fullness of joy!

CHAPTER TWO

Fascinating Facts About How Your Brain Heals

In 1968, Dr. John R. Platt, eminent neurologist, bio-physicist, and social psychologist, announced that rather than the conventionally quoted figure of twelve to fourteen billion brain cells, our brain has more like *one hundred billion* brain cells.

There are about one thousand interconnections or "synaptic junctions" per cell, or about one hundred trillion interconnections in all. If we used some thirty thousand *new* connections every *second* of our lifetime, we could not use them all.

Beyond all of this, in every single cell (this includes approximately ten trillion cells in the rest of the body) the DNA information capacity represents about thirty times the number of letters in the *Encyclopedia Britannica*. To the mathematician, that is about 6 X 10^9. If the DNA in all the ten trillion cells in your body were stretched out end to end, it would reach across the entire solar system![6]

At the close of a class one day in graduate school, I asked my professor, a believer in the theory of organic evolution, "How does evolutionary theory explain the development of a human brain that has the capacity for problem-solving far beyond any need in a lifetime? According to the evolutionary theory an organism develops its equipment only if that equipment is needed." He answered that evolutionary theory had no satisfactory explanation for that. And then he asked, "Why do you think the brain has so much more capacity than we could possibly use in our lifetime?"

I thought I saw a twinkle in his eye when he asked that question, and I guessed that he might be expecting a sermon since he knew I was a clergyman. Of course, I couldn't disappoint him, so I answered, "I believe that when God made the first man in His own image, he didn't intend that he should live for sixty, seventy, or even a hundred years. God planned that man should live for eternity. So he equipped him with a brain that could be fascinated with an infinite universe for a never-ending eternity!" Kindly, but seriously, the professor said, "You may have something there." And of course, I think I do!

I agree with the author who wrote, "Every human being, created in the image of God, is endowed with a power akin to that of the Creator—individuality, power to think and to do. The men in whom this power is developed are the men who bear responsibilities, who are leaders in enterprise, and who influence character. It is the work of true education to develop this power; to train the youth to be thinkers, and not mere reflectors of other men's thought."[7]

It is this uniqueness, this individuality of the human self that has led renowned neuroscientist John C. Eccles to say toward the close of a lifetime of meticulous research,

"Since materialist solutions fail to account for our experienced uniqueness, I am constrained to attribute the uniqueness of the self or soul to a supernatural spiritual creation. To give the explanation in theological terms: each soul is a new Divine creation which is implanted into the growing fetus at some time between conception and birth. It is the certainty of the inner core of unique individuality that necessitates the 'Divine Creation'. I submit that no other explanation is tenable; neither the genetic uniqueness with its fantastically impossible lottery, nor the environmental differentiations which do not determine one's uniqueness, but merely modify it.

"The conclusion is of inestimable theological significance. It strongly reinforces our belief in the human soul and in its miraculous origin in a Divine Creation. There is recognition not only of the Transcendent God, the Creator of the Cosmos, the God in which Einstein believed, but also a loving 'God to whom we owe our being.'"[8]

"I hereby express my efforts to understand with deep humility a self, myself, as an experiencing being. I offer it in the hope that we human selves may discover a transforming faith in the meaning and significance of this wonderful adventure that each of us is given on this salubrious Earth of ours, each with our wonderful brain, which is ours to control and use for our memory and enjoyment and creativity and with love for other human selves."[9]

Some neuroscientists believe that at birth the human brain contains the greatest number of nerve

9

cells that it will ever contain. (This is probably true for most persons, but probably not for everyone as we shall later explain). From that point on these neuroscientists say that brain cells die at a phenomenal rate, particularly in some areas of the brain. It is estimated that the cerebral cortex, including the motor cortex and the frontal lobes, loses about fifty thousand brain cells every day.

There is little or no loss of brain cells as we move slightly farther back and further downward in the brain. While we do not know for certain the major reasons for the demise of these brain cells, we can make an educated guess based on our observations of brain cell loss in late adulthood.

We know that if we fail to use brain cells, they die. This is what was found in a twenty-eight year study of four thousand people in the state of Washington. The principle is clear: **"Use it or lose it"!**

Of course, *disuse,* though possibly the greatest contributor to loss, is not the only contributor. Destructive foreign substances, insufficient oxygen, incomplete and poor nutrition, infectious diseases, inappropriate environments, and head injuries also account for much of this loss. Such loss invites the inevitable consequence—*a broken brain*! Incapacitation, spreading degeneration, mental confusion, perceptual distortion, and a host of emotional disorders! But take heart!

Brain scientists have discovered that the brain doesn't like brokenness!

In fact, when a brain cell dies, the brain immediately dispatches a clean-up crew of *macrophages* to remove the dead debris before it pollutes the brain environment! The brain then orders an army reserve of *astrocytes* to stand ready to "burst" and release *a nerve growth factor* as soon as they receive their orders to do so.

Brain scientists have discovered that the brain is waiting for *us* or *someone who cares about us* to send the orders! We send these orders whenever some caring persons or we put forth continuing and appropriate efforts to *activate* and *energize* our bodies and minds! That is correct! Someone who cares about us or we can activate and energize our body and mind to heal!

I watched a young oriental child who did not have the hearing, the visual, and other large portions of his brain—a child who was not supposed to be able to hear anything, see anything, or do anything but lie paralyzed in his bed for life. I watched this child being rubbed vigorously by a loving mother for extended periods. I watched her support his head and torso as she encouraged him to *try* to crawl,—to *try* to use his arms, his legs. I watched her as she filled his world with beautiful sounds and sights all the time she was vigorously and lovingly rubbing his body. I saw him *crawl*! I saw him *respond* to the sights and sounds about him!

The brain images revealed that his brain had so little development beyond the *brain stem*—that early part of brain development. His brain had so little to offer. Yet, in response to his mother's stimulation, that brain stem actually ordered an army of *astrocytes* to burst and release the nerve growth factors that would sprout new brain pathways and connections to the few remaining undamaged brain territories. These new connections, in new territory, in response to continued and appropriate effort, released new chemicals to release electrical charges and new enzymes to enable that child to use his limbs, his eyes, and his hearing!

I watched a young lady in her early twenties play the piano beautifully *after* her musical brain, and most of the right half of her brain, had been surgically removed! Her surgeons believed she would be paralyzed and bedridden for the rest of her life. But she insisted on learning to play the piano! And with determined, appropriate, and focused effort she did.

There is much more to learn about this *mysterious*, but *awesome* brain. Read on, and discover the principles that you can put into practice or share with others to truly heal a broken brain, and experience the true joy of abundant living!

CHAPTER THREE

How to Control Your Brain For Healing

Their eyes were closed. They were relaxed and inattentive. The electrodes of the electroencephalogram (EEG) were appropriately placed about the skull of each student. In each case we saw what is called a dominant *alpha* rhythm. There were no specific *action patterns* of brain discharges. However, as soon as those students were presented with something to look at and think about, the brain pattern changed. Each EEG recording revealed a different formation of brain patterns of activity. The particular pattern depended upon what the students were looking at. Sherrington described this network as an

"enchanted loom where millions of flashing shuttles (the nerve impulses) weave a dissolving pattern, always a meaningful pattern, though never an abiding one, a shifting harmony of sub-patterns."[10]

Anytime we are attentive we provoke *specific physical space and time patterns* woven by great numbers of nerve impulses in our brain. Brain scientists are agreed on this fact.[11]

We want to harness our thoughts for healing. Like the young oriental child in our last chapter, if we lack the brain cells and networks needed for a task our brain can form them. We can direct our thoughts to the task even as he did. If we already possess the appropriate brain cells and networks for the job, appropriate thinking can move them into action.

Dr. John Eccles and B. Libet have established that specific thoughts generate specific patterns of brain activity. For example, by simply *intending* to move a finger, the 'finger area' of the motor cortex shows an immediate "readiness" change in electrical potential. This decision registered a "readiness potential" in the finger area of the motor cortex about 0.2 s *before* the finger was moved! [12]

A number of studies have recorded other specific brain pattern responses for a variety of other intentions.[13] PET scans have revealed blood flow that is sharply focused in a wide variety of specific locations in the brain depending upon a matching variety of attentions and selections.[14] These clearly affirm the notion that mental events such as focused attention can activate specific nerve events in our brain.

We can postulate that the mind is able by attention to activate any selected parts of the human brain at will. These activated brain parts then give us the "experience" of what we have attended to. These experiences then become the basis of our character and personality. This may be the reason for the divine counsel of the apostle Paul found in his letter to the Romans,

"Do not be conformed to this world, but be transformed by the renewing of your mind, that you may prove

14

what is that good and acceptable and perfect will of God."(Bible book of *Romans,* chapter 12, verse 2.)

An apprehensive clergyman came for therapy. He was hearing voices. He wasn't sure as to whether they were actual voices, or clear and commanding thoughts, —hallucinations or obsessions? He saw nothing associated with the "voices". But he couldn't get rid of the bombarding commands. He was terrified! The bombarding command was "Curse the Spirit, curse the Spirit" repeated over and over again! How could this minister control his brain?

The Bible gives us some very specific instructions. **First** of all, God asks us to

"bring every thought into captivity." [15]

This is possible because God created us with the means for doing it. As we have noted, by an act of our will, our power of choice, we can direct our brain to respond to our deepest desire.

Secondly, we are reminded that this kind of warfare is not with worldly weapons but

"mighty in God for pulling down strongholds, casting down arguments and every high thing that exalts itself against the knowledge of God."[16]

We are in a spiritual warfare. The immanent God in which John Eccles[17] and Albert Einsten believed, empowers our spiritual minds when we have chosen to commit our will to do His will. The apostle Paul, under Divine inspiration reminds us that

"it is God who works in you both to will and to do for *His* good pleasure"(*Philippians 2:13*)

15

In his epistle to the Colossian Christians Paul speaks of this *indwelling of Christ* ("Christ in you") as a great mystery. (*Colossians 1:26-29)* Neuroscientists like J. C. Eccles, Karl Popper, and others have spent years of thought and meticulous research to understand this mystery.

Thirdly, we are asked to bring our thoughts into captivity

"to the obedience of Christ".[18]

The spiritual self can *choose* to yield to Christ OR to the enemy of Christ, once an angel in heaven called Lucifer, but now fallen and called Satan.[19] Both personages can imbue our minds with their thoughts in the spiritual bid for our allegiance. It remains for us to *choose*. Our will is free to choose. Our will is not pre-determined to choose as B. F. Skinner would insist![20]

Furthermore, we are given a specific strategy to use:

"Do not be overcome by evil, but overcome evil with good."[21]

With these principles in mind, I asked the minister to displace and finally totally prevent the bombarding thought from taking over his brain, by repeating a Bible verse that expressed the exact opposite thought and action:

"Bless the Lord, O my soul, and forget not all his benefits."[22]

He was to immediately repeat this Bible verse every time the unwanted command entered his mind. I assured him that if he did it faithfully, he would soon detect the 'strange feeling' he would experience *just before* the unwanted thought bombarded him. His sensitivity to this preceding experience would be increased. He could then repeat that verse, and others like it even *before* the unwanted command entered his mind.

Of course, he was familiar with this Bible verse. But he had never thought of using it therapeutically. I asked him to rehearse this verse in his mind many, many times. I asked him to recall every specific benefit that he could recall receiving. As he recounted these blessings they would bring fuller meaning to those words. Such meaningfulness would activate the emotional response patterns of his brain. In humility he could acknowledge God as the Giver of all of his blessings.

The total response pattern of his brain would enhance his heartfelt praise and his spirit of worship of his God. It would place him within God's army in the spiritual warfare. I asked him to review the entire 103rd Psalm where these verses are found. This would increase his sensitivity to God's many blessings. It would increase his spontaneity to praise and bless the Lord. This affirmed and increased his gratitude for God's blessings. It restored him to a very personal relationship with God. The Bible promises

"The angel of the Lord encamps all around those who fear Him, and delivers them."[23]

In a matter of hours the bombarding ceased. His anxiety disappeared. His countenance brightened. His wife shared her immense relief and joy over the change that had come over him. After a few days of

17

reinforcing therapy along the same line, he was no longer in need of therapy sessions with me.

Nothing tends more to promote health of body and of soul than does a spirit of gratitude and praise. It is a law of nature that our thoughts and feelings are encouraged and strengthened as we express them.[24]

There is healing to be found also in the numerous *promises* made by God and recorded in the Bible. Let's get acquainted with as many of them as we can. Let these promises *direct our attention* to the Divine Creator and the True Physician and Counselor. Let us study the Bible with a view to know God better, and to experience His abiding, indwelling Presence. We can then experience the healing that countless numbers experienced when God the Son walked this earth, and that other thousands are experiencing today.

In our next chapter, we look further into the marvelous *freedom* of our will and its *powerful* role in healing the broken brain.

CHAPTER FOUR

The Power of the Will to Heal

Sometime ago a young college student came to my office for vocational guidance. He was in his senior year, but didn't know what he wanted to do. We chatted awhile, administered a few tests, and drew up a personality-aptitude-interest profile. He scored at the bottom two-percent of his age group for personality integration. His self-concept was ill defined. He did not know who he was. He had no definite plans and no long range goals. He was like a ship at sea without a rudder, and with no port in mind. He had no will to become—only a wish—a fleeting fancy, now and again.

I asked this young man to go back to the dormitory and reflect upon his value system and return the next week with a set of values he felt deeply committed to live by under all circumstances. The next week he came with his list and lines of deep concern across his face. Everything on the list had been crossed off! Handing it to me, he said, "This is terrible. I had to keep crossing my values off because I couldn't see myself sticking by them all the time. I had two left, honesty and fairness, and on my way over here I had to cross *them* out." He had no will to become!

On another occasion a young man came to my office at the insistence of his mother. He had been dismissed from several schools, and was on probation

19

for irresponsible behavior. We drew up a personality profile—his strengths and his weaknesses—and talked about them together. His eyes lit up, energy surged within him as he said, "this is really **me** isn't it—and I've really got a lot of good things going for me if I'd just get hold of these few bad ones—man they're really bad, aren't they (?)—but if I could lick them, I could really become somebody, couldn't I?" In that moment the will to become was born and today he is an electronics engineer, still using his will to become.

The will. What is it? What is its power? And how do we 'strengthen' it?

Dr. William Sadler said, "The will is the sum total of all positive mental activity, the summation of psychic choice and decisions."[25]

Dr. Wilder Penfield, world-famous brain surgeon said, "the will is the spirit of man".

Ellen White wrote, "The will is the governing power in the nature of man, bringing all the other faculties under its sway. The will is not the taste or the inclination, but it is the deciding power which works in the children of men."[26]

"The tempted one needs to understand the true force of the will. This is the governing power in the nature of man, —the power of decision, of choice. Everything depends on the right action of the will. Desires for goodness and purity are right, so far as they go; but if we stop here, they avail nothing. Many will go down to ruin while hoping and desiring to overcome their evil propensities. They do not yield the will to God. They do not *choose* to serve Him.

"God has given us the power of choice; it is ours to exercise. We can not change our hearts; we can not control our thoughts, our impulses, and our affections. We can not make ourselves pure, fit for God, fit for God's service. But we can *choose* to serve God, we can give Him our will; then He will work in us to will and to do according to His good pleasure. Thus our whole nature will be brought under the control of Christ.

"Through the right exercise of the will, an entire change may be made in the life. By yielding up the will to Christ, we ally ourselves with divine power. We receive strength from above to hold us steadfast. A pure and noble life, a life of victory over appetite and lust, is possible to every one who will unite his weak, wavering human will to the omnipotent, unwavering will of God."[27]

My wife and I will long remember our visit with Dr. Wilder Penfield. We spent about six and one-half hours with him. He described some of his experiences in probing the exposed brain of conscious patients undergoing surgery for epileptic seizures. As he would touch the surface of the temporal cortex with a gentle electric current, his patient would relate an experience of many years before. The patient would be re-living that experience all over again. He would see the people, the street corner, the barn—he would hear the sounds, the music, and the conversations that took place years before. It was all there, permanently recorded in the brain ready for playback at the touch of a gentle electric probe.

Dr. Penfield said, "these studies have shown that everything we pay attention to has been permanently recorded in our brain." And then he talked about the **will**. He told us how that even while he was probing with his gentle electric current, he could engage the patient in conversation, and the patient could by the act of his will shut off the effects of the stimulation, not hear or see the playback, and attend to what the doctor was saying. And then Dr. Penfield said, "The will of man is free. It uses the pathways of the brain, but it is not controlled by them. *The will is free.*"

By choosing to attend to Penfield in conversation, the patient was able to shut off all the effects of the electric probe! The physical brain areas impacted by the electric probe ceased to respond! All of this was in response to a simple act of the patient's decision to attend to something else, in this instance his conversation with Penfield.

Ellen White puts it this way: "The power of the will can resist impressions of the mind, and will prove a grand soother of the nerves."[28]

How powerful is the will?

The will is powerful. It is a powerful means of controlling the imagination and resisting disease.[29] The mind and nerves gain tone and strength by the exercise of the will.[30] The power of the will is not valued as it should be.

"Let the will be kept awake and rightly directed, and it will impart energy to the whole being and will be a wonderful aid in the maintenance of health. It is a power also in dealing with disease."[31]

Is the Will an Absolute Sovereign?

Psychiatrist Dr. William Sadler says:

"The will is not an all-powerful sovereign—it reigns on the throne of the mind as the sovereign of a LIMITED MONARCHY—limited by a chemical constitution and biologic by-laws. The eight or ten ductless glands costitute what might be called a 'board of chemical directors'.

"It is not my purpose in calling attention to the role of the ductless glands in human personality and behavior, to discount or belittle the province of the will or the power of decision in the effort to master nerves and to control and direct human conduct. After all, will-decisions are the determining factor in all these struggles. When the ductless gland system is normal, and when its secretions exert a favorable influence upon the nervous system, the individual will find it possible SPEEDILY to conquer his disordered nerves.

"On the other hand, when the endocrines are abnormal, and when their hormones are irritating, overexciting, or unduly fatiguing to the nervous system, the patient has an uphill struggle; his goal of deliverance is farther off, and more persistent and protracted efforts must be made successfully to achieve the conquest of nerves."[32]

There are some who use narcotics, and by indulgence are encouraging wrong habits that are obtaining a controlling power over the will. Others relate to their environments in such a way as to let every influence and every impression determine their choices.

Their will, even in these instances, is still the deciding factor. They have *chosen* to follow these influences.

Because the human mind has become a spiritual battlefield many who fail to yield their will to the Spirit of God have fallen under the rule of Satan. When Satan takes control of person's will, the choices made will lead to pathological outcomes. The brain will suffer from maladies that are foreign to mental health.

One example of an avenue through which Satan tries to access the human mind is through hypnosis. In this practice, one mind is brought under the control of another so that the individuality of the weaker is merged with that of the stronger. The weaker person acts out the will of another, especially if their values are not well established. This is not in God's plan. This only tends to increase the likelihood of the yielding mind to continue yielding to the judgment of others in the future. The will fails to choose the self's highest ideals, and is inclined to follow the lines of least resistance, and immediate satisfactions. From a therapeutic standpoint, we want to encourage the strengthening of the will. We do not want to weaken the will.

What can we do to strengthen the will?

1. Practice deciding things—making up your mind positively, immediately after you have weighed the facts—and stick by your decision, willing to change only when the contrary facts are overwhelming. It is often better to make a mistake, than to sit on the fence of indecision! Sometimes writ-

ing the choice or decision down helps a person stick to the decision they make.

2. Complete each job before you begin another. Don't flit from one thing to another and from one room to another, traveling in a circle.

3. Sometimes games can help develop the ability to decide. I had a young patient who had a reputation among the hospital staff for being excellent at table tennis. But when I played with him, he kept moving back and forth trying to decide when to serve the ball. Once he did, he could really play. Playing that game helped him to make his decision sooner until he could serve with decisiveness.

4. Do something disagreeable that needs to be done by somebody every day.

5. Roll out of bed as soon as you awaken after your planned hours of sleep. Make the decision the night before, and stick to it in the morning.

6. Read deeply and thoughtfully, and stretch your mind to understand and retain what you read.. Excessive reading of emotional fantasies weakens the will.

7. The will is strengthened by exercise—self-denial and self-control. Practice denying yourself of pure indulgences especially when alone.

8. Link your will with Divine Energy by asking God to empower your will.

9. Practice healthful living with good nutrition, exercise, and rest.

10. Make a habit of operating your life by plan, not impulse.

If you find it difficult to put any of the above exercises into practice, begin with the easiest until you have mastered it. Then take the next easiest, and so on. If it is still too difficult for you, try talking to God about it, and ask Him for His power to help you. When you have strengthened your will, you will truly be in charge of your life.

CHAPTER FIVE

How Your Brain Forms Habits

Which shoe did you put on first this morning? You have to think? But you didn't this morning, and you probably put on the same one that you have been putting on first for years—from habit. Wouldn't it be terrible if every time we put on our shoes we had to stop and ask ourselves, "Which one should I put on first?"

Or try this one. Ask a good typist to tell you where the letter M or R is on the keyboard, without looking. Does she have to think? But she doesn't when she types—the habit has been established in her fingers!

Habits can save a lot of time and energy. They are formed by many repetitions. Except for a few simple reflexes, habits are laid down first in the brain, and then in the rest of the body.

The entire brain operates on about 10 watts of power! What fantastic feats are performed on them! On 10 watts of power the brain can perform more math calculations than the world's largest computers.

Let's imagine that a single brain cell fires. It may have just completed a problem in algebra. It analyzed the plus and minus millivolts it has received from a thousand other cells, and made its decision to fire or not to fire. And it does all this in just one thousandth of a second!

So how are habits actually formed in the brain? How do thoughts and words and actions that are repeated over and over again become a permanent part of the brain?

Today we know that messages are processed in the brain and sent to different parts of the body through nerve cells. Each nerve cell is made up of a center called the nucleus, the surrounding fluid called the cytoplasm, and a boundary called the membrane.

Extending from this membrane, many little fibers called dendrites receive messages, and one long sending fiber called the axon, *transmits* messages to the neighboring cells.

Between the sending fiber of one cell and either the receiving *fiber* or *body* of another cell, there is a tiny space called a synapse.

While Dr. Eccles was examining this synaptic junction under an electron microscope, he noticed some tiny enlargements on the sending fiber that looked to him like miniature buttons. So he called them boutons—the French word for buttons. (Figure 5.1, page 34)

Today we know that these little boutons are found in different shapes and sizes. We also know that they secrete various chemicals. One is acetylcholine. This chemical closes the tiny gap, or synapse, and stimulates the next cell to send the message on down the line. (Figure 5.1, page 34)

Brain scientists have discovered that any thought or action that is often repeated is actually building these little boutons on the ends of certain nerve fibers so that it becomes easier to repeat that same thought or action the next time.

Dr. William Sadler tells us that our established habits make literal pathways through the nervous system. He reminds us that frequent repetition of the same thought, feeling or action wears a deeper 'groove', just as repeated walking over a lawn will wear a deep path in the sod.[33]

When visiting with Dr. Wilder Penfield he told me that his studies of brain stimulation in his patients undergoing open-brain surgery have taught him that with each stimulation nervous tissue responds more readily. Physical changes have taken place in the responding nervous tissue as a result of stimulation.

The sobering thought, then, is that *every thought, feeling, or act repeated is producing physical and chemical changes in our nerve pathways,* either to bless or to curse us when these changes have been strongly established. Think of the implications of this fact for our mental or emotional health and our character formation!

"What the child sees and hears is drawing deep lines upon the tender mind, which no after circumstances in life can entirely efface.... Repeated acts in a given course become habits. These may be modified by severe training, in afterlife, but are seldom changed."[34]

Whenever I give a talk on this subject, someone always asks, "Do these boutons ever disappear?" At present it appears that only after *years* of disuse the pathways that contain these boutons may gradually die.

It seems that habits form a rather permanent pathway in the brain. Unless a habit is not practiced at all for many years, it is never erased. Habits can be overcome, however, by developing other habits that are stronger than those that a person wishes to overcome.

We can build new pathways in the brain by consciously choosing to make a different response to a given situation than we have been used to making. We must make that conscious choice so many times that we build more boutons on the new pathway than we have on the old one.

Then when the nerve impulses come flowing through the brain, it will be easier to take the new route rather than the old. It's like this. From the main sending fiber of every cell there are many branching fibers. These are alternate pathways for us to use.

In other words, we choose another route—to feel kind instead of angry, to compliment instead of criticize, to help instead of hurt. And when we resist the temptation to do wrong, another chemical such as GABA is secreted which immediately puts the brakes on.[35]

So many times conflicting messages are stimulating the nerve cell. Some say, "Yes, do it!" Others say, "No, you'd better not!" To fire or not to fire is the question. How does any brain cell know what to do?

Have you ever been tempted with a piece of cake when you promised yourself you were on a diet? You thought, "My, that looks good!" Immediately the coded message backed by, say, 30 millivolts of energy says to your brain action cell, "Fire!"

Just at that moment, you added the thought, "No, I'd better not!" Immediately the chemical GABA is secreted by another pathway coming to your brain action cell. This one is backed by, say 40 millivolts of energy with the message, "Don't fire!" (The stronger your decisiveness, the more the energy reaching the cell.)

The hostess is handing the cake your way, but you've already decided, weakly, by just 10 millivolts of energy. And so, half-hesitantly you say, "No, thanks."

You see, it takes at least 10 millivolts of energy to cause a brain cell to fire. In this case, your action cell did some quick algebraic summations. Thirty millivolts to fire, 40 millivolts not to fire. Net difference: 10 millivolts not to fire!

And if the devil was back of all this effort to get you to break your promise to yourself, he says, "Well, I lost that one, but not by much!" And he lays better plans for the next time. He cannot read your mind. But he can surely read your vacillating behavior.

About a hundred years ago the eminent psychologist William James hinted at the molecular basis of habit in these memorable words: "Could the young

31

but realize how soon they will become mere walking bundles of habits, they would give more heed to their conduct in the plastic state. We are spinning our fates, good or evil, and never to be undone.

"Every smallest stroke of virtue or of vice leaves its never-so-little scar. The drunken Rip Van Winkle, in Jefferson's play, excuses himself for every fresh dereliction by saying, 'I won't count this time!' Well! He may not count it, and a kind heaven may not count it; but it is being counted nonetheless. Down among his nerve cells and fibers the molecules are counting it, registering and storing it up to be used against him when the next temptation comes. Nothing we ever do is, in strict scientific literalness, wiped out.

"Of course, this has its good side as well as its bad one. As we become permanent drunkards by so many separate drinks, so we become saints in the moral, and authorities and experts in the practical and scientific spheres, by so many separate acts and hours of work."

And then, Dr. James adds: "Let no youth have any anxiety about the upshot of his education, of whatever line it may be. If he keeps faithfully busy each hour of the working day he may safely leave the final result to itself. He can with perfect certainty count on waking up some fine morning, to find himself one of the competent ones of his generation, in whatever pursuit he may have singled out. Silently, between all the details of his business, the power of judging in all that class of matter will have built itself up within him as a possession that will never pass away. Young people should know this truth in advance. The ignorance of it has probably engendered more discouragement and faint-heartedness in youths embarking on arduous careers than all other causes put together." [36]

As one visionary and progressive moral educator put it, "We shall be individually, for time and eternity, what our habits make us."[37] There is no mystery about the nature of a person's character. "The character is revealed, not by occasional good deeds and occasional misdeeds, but by the tendency of the habitual words and acts."[38]

Now, suppose that in the process of building a new brain pathway, you should happen to slip back and go over the old pathway again. Perhaps you have had this experience.

You may have lived a changed life for months, and then all of a sudden you act just like you used to. You lose control.

The old devil whispers in your ear, "Aha! You haven't gained anything. You haven't changed at all. You're the same old person." Don't you ever listen to him, because he hasn't reminded you of the victories you have gained in the new pathways. He doesn't tell you about the physical and chemical changes that have taken place in the new pathways of your nervous system.

So when you fall, the thing to do is to get up and start working on the new pathways again. You never lose ground on the new pathway—those boutons are not erased by the occasional fall!

Every success in the right pathway is one less time that you have failed. And eventually you will have developed such a strong response to the right way that it will be very unlikely that you will respond in the old way.

Healing the broken brain—overcoming depression, anxiety, panic disorders, etc.—means developing a new set of healing habits.

So just how do we go about developing healing habits? Is there anything specific that we can do to help set up new pathways in your brain? How can we develop good habits that are stronger than our bad ones? In the next chapter we'll try to answer those questions.

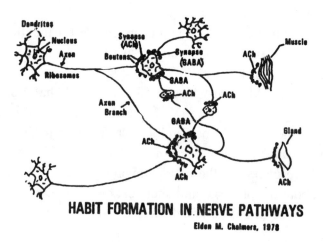

HABIT FORMATION IN NERVE PATHWAYS
Elden M. Chalmers, 1978

Fig. 5.1 Note the boutons and synapse where ACH or GABA is secreted delivering its message. Note the inter-neurons between the two horizontal pathways.

34

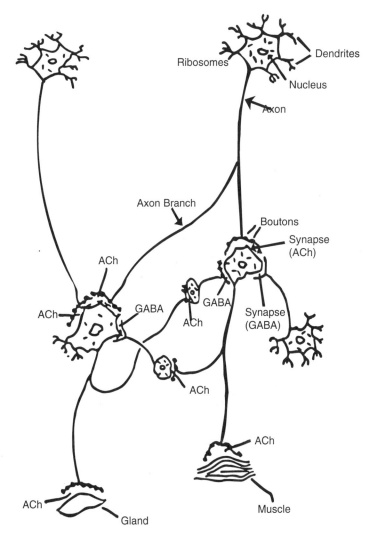

HABIT FORMATION IN NERVE PATHWAYS

Fig 5.1

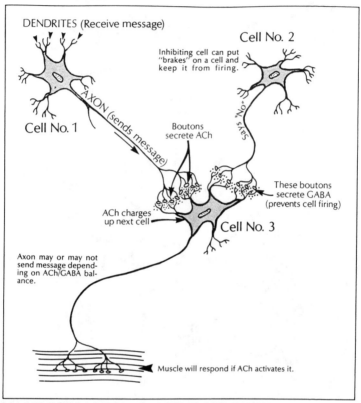

DENDRITES (Receive message)

Cell No. 2

Inhibiting cell can put "brakes" on a cell and keep it from firing.

Cell No. 1

AXON (sends message)

Says "No"

Boutons secrete ACh

These boutons secrete GABA (prevents cell firing)

ACh charges up next cell

Cell No. 3

Axon may or may not send message depending on ACh/GABA balance.

Muscle will respond if ACh activates it.

HABIT FORMATION IN NERVE PATHWAYS Elden Chalmers, 1978

NOTE: Repeated stimulation of cell #1 or #2 matures and multiplies the boutons at the end of their axon.

Cell #1 excites and cell #2 inhibits cell #3. The cell that delivers the most energy by at least 10 mv. determines what cell #3 will do.

Fig 5.2

CHAPTER SIX

Practical Ways to Start a Healing Habit

Do you ever get tired of trying to remember all the things that need to be done? Ever wish others would do their own thinking—remember where they put things, remember their own appointments, remember to get their own things done? You have a hard enough time thinking for yourself, without having to think for everybody else!

Well, it just could be that learning a lot of good habits is just the thing you need. Habits can take a huge load of energy off your mind. Well-established habits are almost completely automatic. They hardly require any thinking at all!

Almost any routine task can be done by habit. Sit down and take inventory of all the regular things you do or should do. Make a list and shuffle the tasks around in the list until you have found the most logical spot for each job. Put together the ones that naturally go together. Tie down the hard-to-remember jobs to things you never forget.

Family worship and times of togetherness can be tied to regular meals, and so can tooth brushing. Clothes will never have to be picked up if they are never laid down. Make the habit of putting them on hangers or hooks right while you are changing your clothes.

Make a habit of every regular task—daily ones, weekly ones, monthly ones, and yearly ones. Tie them all to something else you do that you never forget. Visualize the sequence—see yourself performing the habit at that particular time. Your brain will make clockwork of it all, and you'll save yourself a lot of energy.

Habits can be formed at anytime in life. Infancy and childhood are the most favorable times, of course, to begin forming them. Brain cells that must work together to perform a given task tend to work together in the future.

Association networks involving specific brain cells required for given tasks become established very quickly. These networks resist being rearranged for other tasks. This is one reason that the earliest habits laid down are the most enduring. Repetition, of course, is an even more important reason.

Some habits are easier to form than others simply because we inherit different habit tendencies. Because of the widespread practice of bad habit patterns down through the centuries, bad habits are more easily formed than good ones and are harder to give up once they are formed.

If young children are left to themselves they will learn the bad more readily than the good. As the Bible says we are "by nature the children of wrath"— "the children of disobedience."[39]

Habits, like any other nervous activities, establish themselves in harmony with some rhythmic pattern of the nervous system. It's easy to get sleepy and to awaken from sleep the same hours of the day—to

36

get hungry at the regular meal times—to miss the return of some member of the family at the regular hour. Even the drumming of the fingers on a table or the regular sprees of a drunkard operate in rhythm.

I think you've caught my point. The secret to breaking a habit is to break the rhythm. Or better still, put a good habit in its place, and establish the new habit in rhythm.

I had a patient once who always had a horrible choking sensation every April. A rapist had choked her a few years earlier in the month of April, and every year her autonomic nervous system[40] would repeat the April experience. The cure came when we broke the rhythmic cycle, replacing it with delightful autonomic system responses.

Now let's take a look at a few things we can do to change our habits in a matter of weeks. First, act decisively. Say an **emphatic** "No!" or a **positive** "I will do it!" And those boutons we talked about in the last chapter will form more rapidly. A nerve current travels *faster* when triggered more strongly![41]

Do you know how long it takes a nerve cell to build a complete protein molecule like those that make up the boutons? Just one second! When a strong enough stimulus hits a nerve cell, the cell nucleus sends a message into the surrounding fluid to tiny threadlike substances with instructions to build protein molecules from certain amino acids. And it all happens in just one second of time![42]

Of course, it takes thousands of molecules to form a *bouton*. But the stronger your decisiveness, the more energy you invest in your actions, the *faster* the nerve impulses travel down the pathway(s) to build a new habit or block a repetition of the old. (Fig. 6.1) No wonder Solomon, the wisest man who ever lived said, "Whatever your hand finds to do, do it with your might."[43]

Next, nip the old impulse in the bud while it is still in the making, not when it has fully formed! It is only when you let the threads of thought linger in your mind that your nerve impulses weave a fully-formed image, and travel down the motor pathways of your brain and body to strengthen the old habit.

Many people burn up a lot of nervous energy trying to keep from doing something they want to do, simply because they let these threads of yet-unformed mental images linger in their minds. They toy with them until they travel down to the very end of the motor pathways and build boutons, preparing the way for their downfall at some off-guard moment in the future!

The best way to nip the impulse in the bud is to go right back into the mind, uproot those character-destroying motives, plant the seed of your new purpose, and cultivate that new habit of thinking.

This means settling it in our minds so that instead of saying "I wish I could do it, but I won't," we can *truthfully* say, "I really do *not* wish to do it, *therefore* I will not!" If you have trouble saying that truthfully, ask God to help you. You might discover that He will perform an instant miracle of grace and give you that deep desire! After all, His grace is the source of any power to overcome that we possess.

Never allow an exception to occur! The philosophy that "this once won't hurt" establishes the old habit more firmly. It's the new habit that needs strengthening, not the old!

Try to anticipate those times when the old habit is most likely to overcome you, and deliberately plan to substitute activities for those times. It's the combination strategy of breaking the rhythmic pattern of the old habit, and overcoming the evil with the good![44]

And, incidentally, it's a great trick to displace the old habit by the very opposite kind of habit. For instance, instead of loafing around at every opportunity, plan a good swim, plant a garden, or have a good workout. Instead of criticizing, compliment. Instead of pouting, smile. Instead of complaining, sing! And *plan* for these overcoming tactics ahead of time.

Practice your new habit at every opportunity and in response to every emotional prompting in that new direction. New habits die without exercise. And emotional promptings that are allowed to evaporate

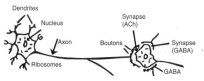

Figure 6.1 Boutons are shown at end of an axon.

soon fail to reappear.

In your efforts to overcome bad habits and to form good ones, don't overlook the power of prayer. But be sure to pray in the positive and to pray in faith. When you ask God for victory over some bad habit, ask Him to bless you with those gifts that are the opposite of the habits you want to overcome. Don't dwell on your bad habits in prayer!

For instance, instead of concentrating in your prayer on what a violent temper you have, confess that temper, but then ask God to help you to be calm, kind, courteous, thoughtful, patient, helpful. As you pray, imagine the emotional experiences associated with these words. Ask God for these gifts and expect to experience them.

Sometimes God has a difficult time with us. We ask Him to help us get rid of our violent temper, and then we dwell on the awfulness of that violent temper so long in prayer that we traverse those nerve pathways that *generate* our tempers. And the opposing positive pathways cannot operate.

Dwell on your failures and victory pathways cannot operate. When failure pathways are operating, the brakes are on the victory pathways. And God can't help you unless you get your foot off the brakes! That's one reason God says that you must pray in faith without doubting or wavering.[45] Praying in faith means focusing on the positive promises of God, not dwelling on the weaknesses of our human flesh! So when you pray, pray in faith for the *new* habit that you want to establish, not about the old habit you want to break. If you have difficulty "praying in faith", like the desperate father who begged Christ to heal his convulsion-stricken son, ask God as that father did, "Lord, I believe; help my unbelief!" God will help you to take your foot off the brakes![46]

You will find it very helpful to spend time filling your mind with the attributes of God at anytime during the day. Meditate upon the meaning of love, mercy, goodness, joy, peace, and temperance. Because

40

these are *spiritual* gifts, they can be yours for the asking. Determine to exemplify them[47] in your life. Study the life of Christ and other Bible characters in their moments of victory. Pray for these same noble qualities. As you pray, imagine yourself in partnership with God generating these same noble qualities. Dwell on them. Your brain will send impulses down all the pathways throughout your body to establish habit tendencies in harmony with your lingering thoughts and intents.

Psychologists have found that skills are more successfully performed when rehearsed in the mind ahead of time. Sports psychologists have assisted Olympic champions overcome their failings with such rehearsals. Physical therapists have helped patients regain the use of their paralyzed hands and other body parts with such rehearsals. Panic disorders, phobias, and obsessions have all disappeared with such rehearsals. In all of these instances, the body is getting ready to respond to every intention of the mind. The pathways are establishing habit tendencies. New nerve growths and new boutons are forming with every rehearsal of the mind. So rehearse your good intentions.

Something else that really helps in changing your habits is to practice balance in your life. Avoid sameness and avoid the extremes. Give your mind and body the needed balancing change. We'll talk more about why this is important when we present our postulates.

Make out a schedule. Look at the past week. What was it like? Was it balanced? Work, play, meals, exercise, rest, study, meditation, worship, and selfless service—were they all in balance?

Bring balance into your day, every day, and you will be better equipped to succeed in the fascinating challenge of changing your habits! There is a two-way relationship between our habits of thinking, feeling, and behaving— and our mental and emotional health!

In our next chapter we shall illustrate this two-way relationship as it relates to the widespread problem of depression. We will give you specific suggestions for dealing with depression: how to *avoid* it and how to *get out of* it.

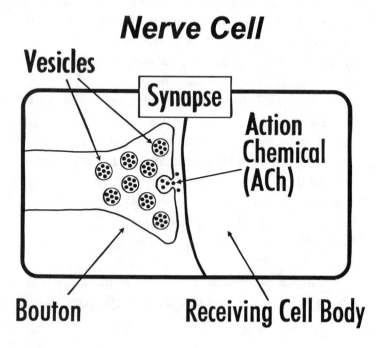

Nerve Cell

Vesicles

Synapse

Action
Chemical
(ACh)

Bouton   Receiving Cell Body

CHAPTER SEVEN

How to Conquer Depression

Depression can happen any time from the cradle to the grave. Even babies as young as seven to fifteen months of age can be depressed. It happens when they are separated from a loving mother, feel emotional neglect or abuse, or sense that the mother herself is downcast and despondent.

Babies become withdrawn and inactive after an initial burst or period of crying, making no demands on their environments and showing increasing feelings of hopelessness and sadness. Sometimes they cry intermittently but are mainly unresponsive and listless. They show feeding disorders, often regurgitating their food and sleeping excessively.

One baby developed a depression because his mother was uneasy about caring for him. Afraid to hold him, she avoided him except for his obvious physical needs. After talking to her pediatrician, she was able to relax and give her baby the warmth and loving care he so much needed, and her baby began to smile and to conquer his depression. Warm, loving care is a vitalizing power. It touches every part of brain and body with healing. Its source is our loving God.

Let's consider depression among the aging. Suicides occur most frequently in men over the age of sixty. Rates for women are much lower. The loss of a sense of personal worth, combined with a hopeless outlook for the future, can trigger depression. The elderly often are unable to accept their new role of increasing dependency, their waning physical strength and flexibility, the loss of some deeply loved person, or apparent or real financial insecurity. The closeness of a new loved one or the genuine caring and cheerful sharing of a son or daughter or younger brother or sister have all helped many of these out of their depression and kept others from even experiencing it.

Even the faithful Christian is not beyond the burden of depression. Job, one of the leading figures of the Old Testament, cried out:

"Why then have You brought me out of the womb? Oh that I had perished and no eye had seen me! ...I was at ease, but He has shattered me ....He pours out my gall on the ground....I have sewn sackcloth over my skin, and laid my head in the dust. My face is flushed from weeping, and on my eyelids is the shadow of death...Though I speak, my grief is not relieved; And if I remain silent, how am I eased? ...My spirit is broken, My days are extinguished ...Why do you hide Your face, And regard me as Your enemy? ... And where is now my hope?"[48]

After one of my lectures on emotional health, someone turned in the question, "Would Elijah [a Biblical prophet] have passed one of your psychological tests as being emotionally healthy?" The rest of the question betrayed the marks of a skeptic deeply prejudiced against psychology and psychologists.

I replied, "If you could go through three years of famine, fed only by the ravens, all the while haunted by the thought that the king's forces were out to kill you; if you could face 450 prophets of Baal thirsting

44

for your life, then, after performing an outstanding miracle to exonerate the God of heaven, learn that the king's wife had vowed you would not live; if your work seemed all in vain; if, only after all this you would suffer a spell of depression, you would probably pass my psychological tests for emotional health with flying colors!" Yes, even Elijah became depressed. But God loved him and sent an angel to sustain him even in his depression.

Life loses its meaning. Anyone who has suffered from depression knows how terrible it is! You feel all alone, and nobody seems to understand. If somebody succeeds in sparking you with hope, the spark quickly dies. It seems as if there is nothing of any use. The other symptoms are many and widely different for different people and different circumstances. One finds concentration difficult, and for some the morning is probably the worst time of the day.

Everything takes extra effort. You feel washed out and tired. You can't make up your mind about anything. And of course you have no ambition or interest in what is around you. You may even feel guilty, and yet not be sure what about—or you may know that many others have felt forgiveness for the same things or worse, but that doesn't help you at all. You just feel sure God has forsaken you, and you may even be scared and cry a lot more or become easily irritated. Perhaps you feel you are about to lose your mind.

Sometimes depressed people sleep fitfully and waken very early, long before they are rested. Others have trouble getting to sleep. They don't feel like eating. They have spells of dizziness and disturbing palpitations of the heart. The symptoms are many, and most depressed people do not experience them all. The symptoms differ for different people and for different circumstances.

What causes feelings of depression? Usually there is a combination of causes. We might be low in blood sugar, low in hemoglobin, or low in thyroid. I have found these three to be the most common physical causes of depression. Some authorities think that there is

> Many factors can cause depression: bad diet, low blood sugar, guilt, repeated failures, and marital or financial difficulties.

in some instances an upset or defect in amine metabolism. But sometimes the problem is not physical at all.

Some incident may trigger off a whole chain of thoughts that exaggerate our failure experiences, and we feel totally incapable and worthless. A surrender of our otherwise highest moral principles in a moment of weakness can trigger the deepest depression with feelings of terrible guilt and unworthiness. I have seen such persons experience extreme sensations of nausea, often followed by vomiting. Repeated financial difficulties, mounting debt, failure in marriage or child training—any of these will tend to drain off nervous energy, disrupt the normal chemical balance, and bring on feelings of depression.

How can we avoid these spells of depression? Nobody has all the answers, and sometimes, like Job, we can't. But here are a few very important suggestions:

Make sure that your meals are eaten at regular times, spaced about five hours apart, and moderate in size. Regularity in your meal schedule is important in regulating blood-sugar levels and in providing your digestive system with its necessary rest. Many disturbed and easily depressed children come from homes where regular mealtime is unimportant. They develop habits of eating "junk food" at all hours of the day or night.

Refined sweets, if used at all, should be used very sparingly. Carbohydrates should come from fruits and whole-grain foods, such as wheat, corn, oats, and millet. Low hemoglobin can usually be prevented by meals rich in iron, vitamin C, and vitamin B_{12}. The highest concentrations of iron, for ovo-lacto vegetarians (those who eat eggs and drink milk) are found in dried fruits, dark leafy green vegetables, whole grains, eggs, and cheese. Eggs and cheese should be used sparingly, however. Adequate amounts of B_{12} are provided by even small daily intakes of milk and cream or cottage cheese. Vegans (vegetarians who do not use dairy products) can provide themselves with B_{12} by using fortified soy products such as vege-burgers, and non-dairy yogurt.

Meals should be eaten slowly and food masticated thoroughly to make good blood. Incidentally, partially digested food that remains in the stomach too long forms alcohol. This happens when we over-eat, drink too much liquid with our meals, or eat combinations of food at the same meal that require widely differing time periods to be broken down and absorbed into the blood stream. Many prescription and nonprescription drugs including cough syrups that have a heavy alcohol base contribute to depression. We will deal with the depressions that are caused by stimulants as well when we get to our postulates. Low thyroid can be corrected by your family physician. So much for avoiding the physiological causes of depression.

Develop the habit of positive thinking

If every member of the family would practice positive thinking about life (see box at the end of chapter), we all would be building our sense of personal worth, and feelings of depression would come less often, and for some people never to any noticeable or incapacitating degree! If they did, for many, they would be short-lived.

In my teens I memorized passages of Scripture that were to become the guiding mottoes of my life:

"I can do all things through Christ who strengthens me."[49]

"Whatsoever your hand finds to do, do it with your might."[50]

"Count it all joy when you fall into various trials; knowing that the testing of your faith produces patience. But let patience have its perfect work, that you may be perfect and complete, lacking nothing." [51]

"Thanks be to God, who gives us the victory through our Lord Jesus Christ."[52]

Encourage the family to find powerful Bible passages like these, memorize them, and share them during family worship. You will be helping to build the emotional health of your family. These suggestions will toughen up your emotional fibres.

A change of environment or activity

But what do we do when depressing feelings and thoughts *hit* us? The moment you sense this happening, deal with them decisively. If possible, physically move out of the spot where you are and think about something you can do with your hands. A change of environment will help you change your thoughts. Deliberately bring your mind to a new task—scrubbing, digging, or planting. Drink a glass of water. Breathe deeply out in the fresh air. Vigorously wash your face and the back of your neck with cold water. Take a warm shower followed by a cold one.

Any of these mechanical methods will tend to shift the circulation of the blood and the firing patterns of your nervous system and make it easier for you to use your willpower to think of the positive, wholesome, and rewarding experiences of your life.

As you do these things, think new, invigorating thoughts. Thoughts get tied into our environments and our activities. The places where you have thought these invigorating, victorious thoughts will tend to trigger them off again.

The late Dr. Wilder Penfield told me that brain centers triggering similar thoughts and feelings are located next to each other and that when one fires, nearby centers tend to fire too. In view of this, it is easy to see why one discouraging thought will trigger off another and still another until all we can think of is something discouraging!

So when this happens, move out of the place where you are thinking these thoughts to help your thoughts tie into more pleasant things. Do something different and resolutely make the effort to change the stream of your thinking. Yes, it does take effort and determination to change our thoughts and feelings— but these mechanical movements will help us to do it.

Depression caused by guilt. If the depression-triggering thought produced feelings of guilt and unworthiness, follow the Bible steps to resolve these feelings of guilt. If you've been holding on to known sin, confess it to God. Apologize if you have wronged someone; and make the supreme decision that regardless of the apparent cost to you, you will use your powers and strength and your God-given energy to get that sin out of your life for all time. Make the supreme commitment to serve God in complete surrender to His revealed will as found in the Bible.

If your feelings of depression are accompanied by feelings of failure and worthlessness, dwell for a few moments upon some of your achievements and successes in life. In fact, during times of discouragement, it's good to review many of these high points of success in your life. Remember, you were made to succeed. And just as a child gets up after falling and learns to walk, so if you will keep getting up to try again, you will achieve success. Incidentally, parents should see to it that children learn to succeed even in small things. Children need to learn to enjoy their successes. Teach them how to do things that will give them a sense of achievement and personal worth. *Minimize their defeats and maximize their successes.*

If the depression was triggered because you were rejected by someone very important to you, get busy lending a helping hand to the unfortunate and needy. Do things for little children and for the aging.

They will appreciate your caring, and you'll begin to feel the joy of being helpful.

Feelings of depression are always characterized by negative thoughts—negative thoughts about yourself, about your circumstances, and about your future. And because these negative thoughts are greatly exaggerated and involve the deepest emotions, they tend to get locked in to reverberating circuits in your nervous system, establishing themselves as habits in the process.

If these feelings of depression build up so strongly and tightly that you can't handle them, seek out good professional help. The sooner you do, the easier it is for the therapist to help you break up the undesirable thought patterns.

How to think positively

HOW CAN we avoid having thoughts that make us depressed?

- **First**, develop the habit of thinking of good things— interesting things: your successes, achievements, opportunities for service, people in need whose lives you can brighten.
- **Second**, develop the habit of looking at every problem and difficulty as a stepping-stone to victory. I have never forgotten a cartoon I saw –when I was just a lad. A young boy with a saw in his right hand looked with dismay at a piece of board with a notch he had just cut out to fit around a post. It was obvious he had cut the wrong side of the board, but I'll never forget the caption of the cartoon. It read: "Even a mistake shows you've tried!" Look at every mistake as something you can profit from—a stepping-stone to success!
- **Third**, feel yourself toughening up the muscles of your character as you tackle the unpleasant tasks, the mundane chores, and the messy jobs. And then, take as your motto, "I'll always be true to my conscience."
- **Fourth**, make a habit of smiling at people from the inside; and practice feeling your happy thoughts toward the people you meet.
- **Fifth**, memorize key Scriptural promises that can carry you through periods of discouragement or despondency.

Healing the Broken Brain
Principles and Postulates

CHAPTER EIGHT

Promoting Psychological Growth

POSTULATE 1. Prescription medicines may interfere with psychological growth.

My phone rang. On the other end was a distraught husband. "Doctor, my wife's nerves are shot, and she continues to get worse. I have spent thousands of dollars on psychiatrists to get her well, and she keeps getting worse. I don't have much money left, but I love my wife, and I don't want to take her to a state hospital. I don't know what to do! She cries a lot, gets upset over what to me is the least little thing. She is always putting herself down. She gets into terrible depressions."

We set up an appointment for an evaluation. The forwarded records revealed a long history of the kind of episodes her husband had described. These records also revealed that the treatment of choice was various medications calculated to address the patient's symptoms--the anxiety reactions and the depressions.

Unfortunately, as is so often the case, even though the patient's initial response to the various medications seemed favorable, her physiological system soon adapted to each medication and shortly thereafter the tranquilizers acted upon her system like stimulants, and the anti-depressants like depressants.

I recalled my psychopharmacology professor showing us slides from patients' charts that graphically described this reversing action of every stimulant, and every tranquilizer after prolonged use.

While such drugs may be useful to remove an incapacitating symptom, most of them have harmful side effects. Some of these side effects threaten the user's life, weaken or destroy body and brain tissue, and upset the delicate chemical and electrical balance of our internal physical and mental processes. Furthermore, in matters of the brain and the mind, a number of studies have convincingly argued that without accompanying appropriate psychotherapy or counseling, cure or restoration to wholeness and true well-being is less likely. Is this because one must enlist the powers of appropriate thinking to bring about true healing? In the pages that follow we will provide abundant support for this thesis.

In the case I have described, I searched for the cause or causes of her problems. Did she have the physiological and psychological resources to cope? If she did, was she using them appropriately? If she didn't have those resources, could we help her acquire them? Were her physical health habits developing both of these kinds of resources? Or was she burning up her resources faster than she was building them up? Did she experience any times in her life when she felt full of faith, hope, and love? We needed to seek for answers to all of these questions.

Studies have clearly shown that the body and the brain constantly affect each other. Both body and brain are very dependent upon good nutrition, adequate physical exercise and periods of rest.

Positive thinking has a healing effect on both brain and body. The spiritual exercise of prayer, worship, faith, hope, and self-less love have each been shown in several independent studies and by several different Bible writers to have a profound healing and health-contributing effect upon both mind and body.[53]

Did she need to learn new ways of perceiving her world? Often clinical psychologists use what they call *cognitive reframing* to teach patients to look at their situation from a different and positive perspective. Long before Freud, Breuer, and Helmholtz, the Bible declared that our perceptions do mold and fashion *us* as well as our *behavior*! :

"But we all, with unveiled face, beholding as in a mirror the glory of the Lord, are being transformed into the same image from glory to glory, just as by the Spirit of the Lord."[54]

"As a man thinketh...so is he."[55]

Did she need to learn new responses to her world? Again, how many of us have experienced either the self-destructive or the self-healing power of our choice of words or actions!

"By your words you will be justified...by your words you will be condemned."[56]

The context of these words of Jesus reveals *two* facts supported by controlled experimental studies: (1) Our words *reflect* and *reveal* our deep-seated thoughts and feelings. Sigmund Freud demonstrated this to be true even for "the slip of the tongue". (2) Our words *make a feedback loop to our brain and body centers that prompted them, compounding* or intensifying our deep-seated thoughts and feelings.[57] Thus, our character and hence predispositions are strengthened for better or for worse!

I wanted to heal the *patient*, not just the *symptom*. We will continue the story of this patient later.

As we pointed out earlier, with a hundred billion brain cells, trillions of interconnections among these cells, and the unfathomable potential for developing further trillions of new connections, the brain is designed for growth. This design for growth is limited only by our present state of mortality and our lifestyles.

Recall that in the course of our lifetime more than eighteen million of these brain cells and their connections die *every year* because of **disuse** and **abuse**. The fact that the rate of loss *decreases* dramatically in the lower parts of the brain suggests that **disuse** may be a major cause of brain cell loss. These lower areas of the brain are used for every movement we make no matter how small. Unless totally paralyzed we are using these areas almost continuously.

For psychological health to thrive, *constructive metabolism*,[58] more commonly called *anabolism*, must exceed *destructive metabolism* or *catabolism*. The - *chemical distribution* and *activity* together with the *biological distribution* and *activity* must contribute to constructive metabolism.

Our lifestyle determines whether this metabolism will be constructive or destructive. It is simply stupidity to defend our health-destroying practices by telling ourselves "Oh, well, we all have to die sometime anyway". Such a philosophy prevents the rich and abounding quality of the life we could have.

I was walking toward the college auditorium in Avondale, Australia to address the students. A young man in his late teens or early twenties shouted from some distance behind me, "Dr., are you the Dr. Chalmers who wrote that article on the brain in the magazine *Insight*—'Programming Your Memory Bank'—? "When I said, "Yes, I am" he added, "That article changed my life. I was into drugs and the whole bit."

By that time he had caught up with me, and as we continued our walk to the auditorium, he continued, "My mom had laid that *Insight* on the table with the picture of the brain and the title of the article 'Programming Your Memory Bank'. When I read that article, I thought, 'man, if I've got a brain like that, I'm going to quit messing it up with drugs'. I quit, and decided to go to college and make something of myself. That's why I'm here."

We know that by focused thinking and appropriate actions new growth takes place in the brain. Among the aging, for example, it has been found that new brain connections and networks are formed as the aging keep active, pursuing new learning experiences. Lost abilities due to brain damage and brain cell loss have been regained by well-directed psychological and physical therapy. The

59

psychologically broken and the physically broken brain can experience true healing!

Use your brain in healthy ways, and its cells will sprout and multiply new connections for increased productivity and abounding health. Let your brain cells remain *unused* or *abused* and relevant brain cells and their connections die.

Psychological health implies *growth*, not mere survival, or the *appearance* of a cure because a *symptom* of a psychological disorder is temporarily removed!

Often we must resort to emergency procedures to *cope* in the immediate present. We may need the help of a physician or psychiatrist for a drug prescription to temporarily remove an incapacitating symptom. It is most difficult to control your thoughts, to imagine positive emotions, or to engage in essential health-producing exercises when in a manic or depressed state, when filled with excessive anxiety, plagued with guilt-feelings, obsessed with unwanted thoughts, or the like.

However, it is important to keep in mind that while the removal of a disturbing symptom *may help us to focus on healing efforts*, that removal of the symptom may require other efforts of the body to protect itself for survival. The body often adjusts to the medication. But often the adjustment is temporary. The prescribed drug may actually be upsetting the healthy chemical balance and threatening the survival of vital brain mechanisms, both physical and chemical.

Medical science is offering the best it has, but biochemical science is still searching for better answers! The survival adjustment that masks the disturbing symptom may be the brain or body's best effort to counteract the life-and-health-destroying drug. But in the adjustment process the *quality* of life and health may be compromised. For these reasons, whenever we possibly can, we need to avoid the use of any medications that merely alleviate the symptom.

I applaud the neuroscientists for persisting in their drug research to replace those drugs that have so many harmful side effects with drugs that do not have as many. I applaud other neuroscientists who are documenting the powerful healing effects of appropriate focused thinking and physical stimulation.

We must not lose sight of the fact that we have yet much to learn about the delicate and perfect balance of neuro-chemical activity in a healthy brain. Doctors are well aware of the side effects of their prescription drugs. In fact, often the choice of medication is determined by both its "main effect" and its rather strong side-effect.

For example, if an anti-depressant is prescribed because the patient complains of being depressed and displays those symptoms, but also complains of being unable to sleep, the doctor will likely prescribe a medication whose main purpose is to lift the person out of a depressed mood. There are several antidepressants that will do that about equally well. But their side effects are very different. When depression is accompanied by insomnia the doctor may choose the antidepressant with a stronger sedating effect to help the patient sleep. It is clear that the doctor in this case is treating two of the *symptoms,* but not the depression. The depression is, in fact, affecting the entire system. By treating the symptom, while bringing apparent, but temporary relief, other symptoms go unnoticed or are not perceived to be related to the depression. Healing processes are thwarted, and the neuro-chemical system suffers from aggravated imbalances that threaten its survival. It seems wise to move cautiously in our research in the use of medications lest we unwittingly upset the healing balance in our neuro-chemical system beyond re-adjustment!

The brain has its own pharmaceutical laboratory. Except for genetic anomalies, if we take care to healthfully manage it, our brain will deliver the correct prescription to the correct address whenever it is needed! That dynamic contributes to psychological health and quality growth.

Principle: Any psychological value or technique that would contribute to high quality psychological health must contribute to quality growth.

If medication is deemed to be necessary, we must immediately proceed to set into motion the processes that contribute to psychological wholeness. These processes will be psychological growth processes. New health-producing psychological forces will replace debilitating and destructive psychological forces. We must learn to develop a truly healthy life-style.

Many physicians have tried to persuade their patients to embark on a truly healthy life-style program. Patients that have disciplined themselves to cooperate with these new life-style programs have benefited tremendously. But some patients preferred the "quick fix" of a pill. They would leave these physicians for others that would prescribe their desired drug for that "quick fix". Unfortunately, all too often the drug, while relieving the most disturbing symptoms, would in their side effects be working against the healthy functioning of the brain and body.

Traditionally, for both medicine and psychoanalysis, health is regarded simply as the absence of disease, defect, or disorder. And at the present stage of progress in the medical treatment of emotional disorders, in most instances even psychiatrists[59] must settle for *management* of the disorder, not *cure*. In classical or biblical Hebrew, however, health is typically synonymous with *restoration, to make whole, to cure thoroughly.* When Hebrew biblical scholars used the term for *medicine* they did not use it as a treatment for *symptoms*, but as a *medicine* to *restore completely,* to *wholeness*, and to *cure thoroughly*, to *cure to perfection*. In this book, we shall use the term *health* in the classical Hebrew sense.

The treatment principles set forth in this book, if implemented by the client, will set the client on a journey toward that goal of genuine wholeness[60] and complete restoration.[61] In our mortal state we may not achieve our goal of a complete cure. But we shall definitely move toward it. We shall be on a journey toward genuine wholeness. For the few cases that require the treatment of symptoms, we seek *temporary* relief so we can focus more clearly and strongly upon actions that contribute to restoration and wholeness. Our goal is restoration and psychological wholeness.

Actions that lead to restoration and wholeness facilitate not only the birth, but also the growth, and multiplying of psychological resources. And these all grow and multiply in healthy balance with each other. *How* our psychological resources are formed, grow, and multiply has been shown in chapters two through five.

Resources for growth are those *assets* or *faculties* that, if used as intended by the Creator, *promote growth*. These might be our talents, our thinking and learning abilities, our favorable personality traits, our pure motives.

In our earlier chapters on the forming of good habits we have shown in a preliminary and limited way *that* they promote healthy psychological growth. We have also seen how the very process of developing these positive faculties *inhibits* or shuts down faculties and internal experiences that destroy. The brain structure that incorporates the *interneuron* system[62] provides for this dual action of resources. How wonderfully we are made![63]

Faith, hope, and love contribute to neuro-chemical balance and health of mind.

Faith, hope, and love are examples of resources for growth. They also qualify as underlying *principles* for psychological health. Studies reported by Jeanne Achterberg and G. Frank Lawlis,[64] Joan Borysenko,[65] and others show that negative thinking is an example of one kind of experiencing that tends to destroy. Misdirected hate, envy, greed, generalized pugnacity are other examples.[66] [67]

When people exercise faith, their immune system rallies, wiping out destructive foreign invaders. At the same time, the faith flowing neuro-chemical pathways shut down the pathways that would trigger debilitating doubt.

When people are filled with hope, the brain's "hope pathways" will activate an array of positive and exhilarating emotional experiences and productive activities. Those same activated pathways will at the same time shut down the brain pathways that would interfere with those positive experiences.

Genuine faith is not unreasonable. Repeatedly Jesus healed people so that they might believe that He also has power to forgive them.[68] Faith is our conviction about realities that we cannot see[69], and this conviction must be founded upon knowledge, a knowledge based upon God's Word[70]. As a means of developing a transforming and enduring faith, there is no substitute for the regular and earnest study of the Bible.

The Nature and Power of Love

"There is no fear in love; but perfect love casts out fear, because fear involves torment. But he who fears has not been made perfect in love."[71]

"Love suffers long and is kind; love does not envy; love does not parade itself, is not puffed up; does not behave rudely, does not seek its own, is not provoked, thinks no evil; does not rejoice in iniquity, but rejoices in the truth; bears all things, believes all things, hopes all things, endures all things." [72]

Earlier in this chapter we said that in a healthy brain, appropriate brain chemicals are secreted in just the right amounts and in the right locations. Here is one example: the brain chemical *oxytocin* secreted in abundance in the frontal lobe as evidenced by the abundance of *oxytocin* receptors found there, is associated with *true love* and *fidelity*. When we activate and strengthen those true love pathways in the frontal lobe, a whole array of destructive emotions are held in check, —destructive hate, envy, fear, greed, sexual promiscuity, marital infidelity, spousal and child abuse, —to cite just a few! These are the findings of neurological and psychological studies. I see such scientific data as the handwriting of God in human nature, often clarifying previously recorded revelations in the Bible.

Principle: Faith, hope, and love are essential to quality psychological healing.

We need to promote positive psychological growth. Our psychological health depends upon it.

POSTULATE 2. The Brain Is Prepared for Repair and Growth

The brain has the ability to adapt and change. We are not necessarily stuck with the way we were born or brought up. We are not necessarily the lifelong victims of our genetics. We are not necessarily the victims of a bad start in life. Our destiny is not necessarily determined by the hands of those who shaped us during the first few years of our life. We need not be the permanent victims of our own bad choices and practices.

Even when large areas of the brain are missing because of birth defects, injury, or disease, the brain recognizes this loss and is prepared to develop the lost capacities in the brain areas that remain. For example, the normal brain assigns two primary areas for speech in the left hemisphere.

One of these areas is called Broca's area, named after the scientist who located it. It is located in the front part of the brain and on the left side. The second speech area is called Wernicke's area and is located further back in the temporal lobe, but still on the left side or in the left hemisphere of the brain.

Broca's area retains information about the details of grammar and the proper organization of words into fluent speech. Damage to this area leads to difficulty in speaking fluently, especially in using pronouns, conjunctions, and prepositions. Wernicke's area processes the meanings of sounds. This area brings meaning and understanding to the words we hear.

If Broca's area is damaged the person is unable to speak. If this person's Wernicke area is healthy, he can understand speech, but cannot express that understanding. (*Fig. 8.1, Page 75*) On the other hand, if the Broca's area is healthy and the Wernicke's area is damaged, the person can jabber on and on without understanding. Their speech is like a "word salad"—a fluent expression of meaningless jargon.

Appropriate re-training with methods not unlike those used to teach very young children to learn to express themselves properly can result in restoring the lost ability. Such retraining can either restore the healthy functioning of Wernicke's area or develop a new cluster or network of cells to do the job. Such is the plasticity of the brain. The brain is prepared for repair and healthy growth.

The brain's plasticity or capacity for compensation and the growth of new connections provide hope for the victims of their brain's maladies. Loss of abilities, loss of emotional control, loss of memory, confused thinking, may not have to shape your destiny. The brain's plasticity offers promise for healing.

All too often people feel ashamed, embarrassed, or guilt-ridden over their losses. Their search for causes often ends in putting the blame on their genes, or the way they were brought up, or their own reckless lifestyle. Some people resign themselves to a bleak future. Others think suicide. Still others vent their anger on a world that they feel is responsible. And fortunately, there are those who are aggressive, who take action, who seek solutions for their handicaps.

Don't jump to conclusions about the causes of any mind problems. The causes are almost never singular. Typically they are many and the interactions between them have eluded the best of minds. Most of the causes have probably been beyond our immediate control. We don't typically punish ourselves for developing cancer, diabetes, or arthritis. But we can take steps to reduce the probability of such disorders taking full control of our lives.

We need to take responsibility for those aspects of our lives that we can do something about. As the apostle Paul put it, "Forgetting those things that are behind, and reaching forward to those things which are ahead"[73]—we can take responsibility for these actions.

We can take responsibility for our choice of lifestyle—our nutrition, our exercise program, our rest periods, our use of fresh air and pure water, our attitudes, our values, our habit styles, our priorities, our goals. We know that all of these affect the healthy functioning of our brain.

Again, we must not punish ourselves for the occasional neglect or sinful indulgence—these *may* mete out their own punishment,[74] but the occasional neglect or sinful indulgence does not establish habits in our brain networks, nor do they determine our character.[75] Let's not worry about past wrong-doing! We cannot unscramble eggs!

69

God tries to reassure us that He knows when our spirit is willing but the flesh is weak.[76] Instead of dwelling on our failures, let us mend our ways and pick up again wherever we might have failed! Remember the Bible proverb,

"For a righteous man may fall seven times and rise again, "[77]

And for those readers who might wonder if disordered minds or emotions might be the wrath of God visited upon them, note the assurance of Jesus,

"For God sent not His Son into the world to condemn the world, but that the world through Him might be saved. "[78]

It is true that some Bible verses have been interpreted as though mental illness is a punishment God gives to sinners, or is the tormenting experience of demon possession. One example of such a reference is in the first book of Samuel, chapter 16, verses 14-16:

"Now the spirit of the Lord departed from Saul, and an evil spirit from the Lord tormented him. And Saul' s servants said to him, "Behold now, an evil spirit from God is tormenting you. Let our Lord now command your servants, who are before you, to seek out a man who is skillful in playing the lyre: and when the evil spirit from God is upon you, he will play it, and you will be well. "

A study of the personality and character of Saul reveals that Saul allowed himself to develop the characteristics of bipolar depressives with paranoid features. His love and desire for praise and self-exaltation were allowed to have a controlling influence over his actions and thoughts. His standard of right and wrong became the low standard of popular applause. He opened his heart to the spirit of jealousy when he witnessed the popularity of David. He allowed himself to develop the delusion that David would usurp the throne. He allowed his impulses to control his judgment, until he was plunged into a fury of passion. He had paroxysms of rage that made him ready to take the life of any that dared oppose his will. From this agitated frenzy he would descend into a state of despondency and self-contempt, and remorse would take possession of his soul.

In this time of despondency, self-contempt, and remorse Saul could find temporary relief and a lifting of his spirits as David played upon his harp for Saul. The sound of David's music activated those areas in Saul's brain that lifted his spirits.

Saul's servants were well acquainted with the signal manner in which God had indicated his choice of Saul as the first king of Israel. They knew also that Saul's destiny was in God's hands, and that God was still in charge of the affairs of Israel. Therefore, it was only natural for them to conclude that the distressing or evil spirit that tormented him was from the Lord. Anything permitted by the Lord was understood as coming from Him. Natural consequences of violating God's laws are seen as coming from God.

However, Saul's choice to reject the loving, gentle prodding of God's Spirit to humbly trust God for wisdom and success in ruling Israel and in overcoming the surrounding pagan nations placed him on the side of Satan, that evil spirit. Satan prodded Saul's cultivation of personal pride. It was on that very point of pride that Satan fell from his former God-exalted position as Lucifer in Heaven.[79]

Here is a clear example of how the laws governing mental stability reveal how God works, because God operates those laws. By God's moment by moment involvement in our lives, His laws operate.[80] It is natural that when God's law of love in the human heart is rejected that the very contrasting spirit of evil—e.g., personal pride, jealousy, hatred, and murder—should replace it.[81]

Thus, rather than Saul's mental illness being a punitive affliction arbitrarily imposed by God, it was a lawful and predictable consequence of Saul's indulgence of pride, jealousy, hatred, and paranoid thinking. These same personality traits are present in the psychological profiles of bipolar depressives with paranoid features today. This should provide us with some insights into the contributing causes and the remedies for bipolar depression with paranoid features.

My first bipolar depressive patient with paranoid features would plummet into his depression after reading a brief newspaper account of a farmer in a neighboring province who had more acreage than he had! I knew very little about treating such a disorder, but because he was a religious person, I shared the Lord's promise "He that is faithful in that which is least, is faithful also in much." We focused on several Bible passages that point to the consequences of pride, and the contrasting rewards promised to the humble. Several specific exercises calculated to re-orient his focus in life along the lines of placing his complete trust in God, and self-less service to others were included in the treatment program. His wife joined in helping him to implement these. Many years later, both of them attested to the fact that he never suffered a relapse but enjoyed a productive life of self-less service to others. I believe that God had directly intervened and brought him healing during that single intensive therapy session.

Exercises that aid the development of a healthy humility, a simple trust in God, caring for others, and doing good to one's enemies can bring healing from bipolar depression with paranoid features.

The beautiful consequence of personality trait adjustments is that the malfunctioning brain centers can function healthily once again. Such is the plasticity of the brain.

No one plagued with any mental disorder should be scorned or rejected. God has not rejected them, even though they may have violated His laws that were designed to maintain a healthy brain. However, we should all expect to pay at least a discounted price for our violation of the laws that govern the health and well being of our brain and body.[82] But thanks to our merciful God, He has provided for restoration and healing in the plasticity of the brain he has given us. And we can thank Him for the clarifying support of good science. We can thank God for increasing our knowledge of His laws for

73

thriving health. God's spirit of love, forgiveness, and mercy is written in the plasticity of the brain!

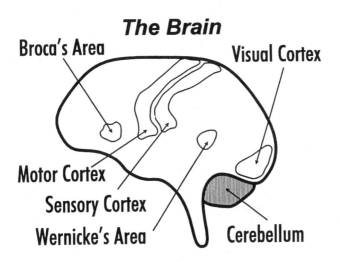

Fig. 8.1 The Broca and Wernicke speech areas.

POSTULATE 3. Internal Harmony Means Psychological Health.

A newly married woman told her counselor, "I know I shouldn't leave my husband for this other man. My husband is really good to me. But I feel a strong urge to leave him and go to this other man. I know that when I was dating, I could never stay with any guy very long. I don't know what's wrong with me, but I can't help it. I just feel driven to try another man!"

Her personality test[83] revealed a very emotionally unstable woman. She was a daring, incisive person who was a law unto herself, and frequently depressed. Her motivational analysis test[84] revealed an excessive craving for romance and affection far beyond any likely achievement of satisfaction. To face this reality was too overwhelming. Her fruitless efforts to satisfy this unrealistic craving drove her ever closer to emotional exhaustion and breakdown.

Her inner conflict made her unstable. She was like the troubled sea when it cannot rest.[85] The winds and tides of external circumstances too easily affected her emotions. She could not remain calm and emotionally stable when there were adversities. She insisted on "being her own boss", but she could not be. Her hyper-reactive

> **Conscience & Submission:**
> "It is necessary to submit to the authorities, not only because of possible punishment but also because of conscience."

76

emotional system and a troublesome world enslaved her.

Compounding her problem was her willfulness—an unwillingness to defer to laws that govern any stable society. She preferred instead to seek out those who would tolerate her emotional unpredictability, and permit her to have her way.

As is so often the case, her conscience bothered her enough to be annoying during these times of willfulness. Research psychologists Cattell and Gorsuch have presented empirical data on the moral structure in societies showing that a general morality factor *does* exist extending across behavior in some 52 countries of quite varied cultures.[86] Cattell's 16 P.F. test of personality structure was used to measure this lady's "conscience" factor.

> **Principle: Purity of purpose and integrity underlie all true harmony of thought, emotion and behavior.**

Her wishful fantasies of romance never became reality. They couldn't! Every new "crush" proved to be a crushing disappointment. She refused to consider the tested and proven principles that she so desperately needed if she was ever to experience inner calm and restfulness. Her compromising mind needed purity of purpose and integrity.

Purity of purpose and integrity are essential foundation principles underlying the harmonious interaction of one's internal resources. They bring peace and calm to the mind and emotions.

Moral Impurity and Troublesome Restlessness:

"But the wicked are like the troubled sea, When it cannot rest, Whose waters cast up mire and dirt."[87]

"Sin is the transgression of the law."[88]

All brokenness of the brain, physical and psychological, all pain, all suffering and sorrow, are the results of law transgressed. The wonderful human machinery has been tampered with, and its delicate mechanism has been made to run counter to the law of its life and endurance. Disease and death are the result.[89]

The energy in the brain is most productive and most efficient when there is harmony inside of us.

Mental conflict, feelings of frustration, and inner tension all "burn up" nervous energy wastefully. "A house divided against itself cannot stand." Often the emotionally disordered person is suffering inner turmoil because of conflicting interests, incompatible values, or values incompatible with their pleasure-seeking or sensual desires. Often their drives are at war with each other, giving them no peace of mind or rest of nerves. Fears of failure, of rejection, of making the wrong decision or the wrong move often fuel this inner turmoil in the midst of these incompatibilities.

Anxious people can find peace by
  (1) examining how they are using their internal resources,
  (2) making the decision to be true to the values of purity and integrity,
  (3) renouncing all contaminating influences,

(4) using their talents and internal resources harmoniously i.e., in ways that are not in conflict, and

(5) keeping their mind stayed on the Lord.

If a therapist is assisting an anxious client, the therapist must be a person whose own internal resources are used harmoniously. The principles of purity and integrity must be *the therapist's* foundation principles. You cannot pull clients out of the swift running current if your own feet are on slippery ground. You cannot pour out of an empty bucket! You cannot write with a pen that is dry!

The approaches a therapist uses will vary from client to client and from therapist to therapist. A psychologically healthy therapist can adapt more readily to a wider variety of patient types, using approaches that best fit the patient. Christian therapists would do well to practice the biblical counsel in this regard.

"And of some have compassion, making a difference: And others...pulling them out of the fire; hating even the garment spotted..."[90]

Patients differ widely in temperament, in their capacity for insight, in their readiness to learn, in their openness to change, in their imaginativeness, etc. Clients have different tender spots, different sensitivities. The skilled therapist will use approaches that are best calculated to fit the client. "One size" doesn't fit all!

Whatever course is followed, the goal of healing therapy is to mobilize our internal resources for *harmonious* action.

POSTULATE 4. The Growing Edge Is the Healing Edge.

Psychological growth begins at the growing edge of our psychological self. We are defining the "growing edge" as the *healthy* perception, attitude, emotion, or personality characteristic that exists beneath any unhealthy expressions. Unless our unhealthy characteristics are removed and our healthy characteristics are nurtured, we will continue to make poor adjustments in life.

Corollary #1: In order for growth to take place, the growing edge must be identified.

In a couple therapy session, the wife retorted angrily after interpreting her husband's statement as a "put-down" on her. Noting his readiness to fight back at that point, but before he said another word, I interrupted with:

"Did you mean to say it that way?"

I had detected from what he had said earlier that his intention was to communicate the reason for the actions for which he had been criticized severely, and I suspected that his reason would be understandable if he could just say it differently. My question led him back beyond his hurtful way of saying it, to his motive or reason, which happened to be a reason springing from his best of intentions in behalf of his wife.

His poorly phrased statement was maladaptive. It contradicted his healthy motive. It falsely communicated his good feelings toward her. If

80

accepted in heart by his wife, his statement would be "tissue" on which nothing healthy could grow.

On the other hand, the motive behind the statement was productive for growth for him as well as for the relationship. It was "the growing edge" for him as well as for their relationship. If he phrased his remark to clearly communicate his good motive, his remark would "attach" to that good motive adding a healthy bit of growth to his psychological self. If accepted in heart by his wife, his properly phrased statement would attach to *her* "growing edge" (her desire for goodness), and provide additional "tissue" for her continuing healthy growth.

At other times, the motive that would prompt such a remark might have been hate. That would have been maladaptive psychological "tissue". One would need to work back from that hate to explore the issues that have spawned it until the "growing edge" was found.

Incidentally, when a couple "makes up" after a fight, they have typically located their "growing edge". If diligently nurtured, their personalities and their relationship will prosper in psychological health and happiness.

It is my belief that every person has plenty of "growth edges"— intellectual power, spiritual power, the desire for goodness, a perception of right, — to name a few.[91] But all too often, somewhere we have developed diseased tissue instead.

The Bible describes our diseased "tissue" as natural to our fleshly nature. We have inherited the tendency to develop diseased "tissue"—a broken brain! God does not condemn us for this tendency. Rather, God invites us—yes, urges us to come to Him for healing and for a new nature. Often, he demonstrates His power to heal us so that we may believe that He also has the power to *forgive* us for our contribution to our brokenness.[92] We come to Him by prayer. The Bible teaches that healing and a new nature are brought about through the work of the Holy Spirit. Without this work of the Holy Spirit our inherited and cultivated tendencies will eventually overpower us, and invite disease and brokenness!

At times we may wish to seek out a therapist to help us locate our "growing edge" He (or she) could do this by "working backward" through our maladaptive ways of coping with a particular problem until the edge of healthy growth is found.

Some people are able to locate their own growing edge, —by reflection, working backward through our maladaptive ways of coping with a particular problem until we find the edge of healthy growth. Like asking oneself, "Do I like myself this way?" " Do I want to act like this?" "Do I want to feel like this?" "How do I want to act?" "How do I want to feel?"

By focusing on how you like to be, to act, to feel, —you will be uncovering your growing edge. Nurture that feeling, that kind of behavior, that kind of attitude. Ask God to forgive you for all that you feel sorry about. Then ask God to give you what He wants to give you. David prayed, "Create in me a new heart, Renew a right spirit within me, and do not take Your Holy Spirit from me."[93] Not a bad prayer for any of us!

If one has avoided using maladaptive ways of coping, but is simply frustrated, unable to discover suitable healthy ways to further growth, take a deep breath of fresh air, go for a walk to clear out "the cobwebs". Take time out for reflection, self-examination, and even a prayer for insight, for understanding, for a renewal of the right spirit within, for the courage to acknowledge one's wrong. When you discover your "growing edge", graft on the new and healthy growth, and move on from there.

You may know other persons much like yourself with similar resources and problems that seem to have found victory. Talk with them. They may have just the suggestions you need.

Some of my clients have found the Bible to be a rich resource of positive thinking, and of promises that they have memorized and meditated upon. As they approached or entered a situation that would ordinarily prove to be a bad experience for them, they would rehearse these passages, building on their growing edge.

And let me assure you from my own experience, that of thousands of others, and from the authority of God's Word, that God will *always* make a way for you to handle any situation when you go to Him in prayer.[94]

Some years ago I inadvertently provoked the wrath of one of my superiors when I transferred to another job. He wrote me a very irate letter about the incident. I shared the letter with my new boss, and I appreciated his counsel. He simply smiled and quoted a Bible passage, "A soft answer turneth away wrath."[95]

I knew that verse very well, and this next one as well: "Pleasant words are as an honeycomb, sweet to the soul, and health to the bones." [96] But my irritation over the letter had blanked them from my memory! After that reminder, however, I had no problem deciding to respond with a soft answer.

But before I formulated my response to his letter, I decided to put myself in his place and see the situation through his eyes.[97] As I did, I could readily understand his feelings, and it was easy to apologize! Here are two other verses providing insights for interpersonal relationships:

"All the ways of a man are clean in his own eyes; but the Lord weigheth the spirits." "When a man's ways please the Lord, he maketh even his enemies to be at peace with him."[98]

If in treatment with a professional, be open about what you feel you can and cannot do. The professional needs to know your psychological resources and your limitations. Don't hesitate to share what your values are. The professional is more likely to suggest options that are realistic for you.

In addition to the information gleaned from verbal interactions with you, some therapists will use psychological test data and background history to help uncover your resources and limitations. They can then provide you with an assignment or prescription that is most appropriate for you.

A word to therapists: There are those who are locked into a severe emotional disorder and cannot discover their growing edge without the help of a skilled therapist.

The process of locating the growing edge is most often a dialogue, incorporating all the skills of counseling or psychotherapy that create a relaxed openness on the part of the client. The therapist's positive, empathic regard for the client, genuineness, credibility, flexibility and openness to the client's points of view, all contribute to the discovery of the client's growing edge.

Corollary #2: Our unhealthy defenses must be removed, much as diseased tissue must be removed in the surgical field, before new healthy tissue can grow. *Denial, learned helplessness, blame,* and *causeless ill-directed anger* are examples of unhealthy defenses that must be removed before the growing edge can be found.

People go to counselors for many different reasons. Some out of curiosity because they've heard good things about the counselor. Others because they think that they'll get some support to get certain others off their back. Some because they think that if they had just the right information they could make it on their own. Then there are those who go for therapy because they are desperate over the course their life is taking.

Many people know that they cannot find the source of healing by themselves. Sometimes this is because all parts of their being—the intellect, the emotions, the will and power of choice are contributing to the spread of "the disease". Every part of their being has become a part of the disease.

This is how some therapists describe *addiction,* and it is akin to how the Bible describes the permeating effects of "sin" which is nothing other than the violation of God's laws of life and health[99]:

> "The whole head is sick,
> And the whole heart faints.
> From the sole of the foot
> even to the head,
> There is no soundness in it,
> But wounds and bruises
> and putrefying sores;
> They have not been closed
> or bound up,
> Or soothed with ointment."[100]

If you feel that your emotional problems have gotten beyond your control, it is very possible that they have affected every part of yourself. You need to seek for help outside of yourself.

Some of my clients have gone directly to the Great Physician. The Bible reports that He healed all kinds of diseases, physical, mental, and spiritual. These clients believed that if there is going to be any healing at all, God would do the healing. In simple faith they have asked God for healing, and for wisdom and understanding to know what they might do for themselves. Their prayers were answered, and they found Him to be One who "forgives all sins and heals all diseases."[101].

Others have chosen to go to a reputable therapist, and have found the healing they were looking for.

To remove 'diseased psychological tissue', some therapists are comfortable with only one method— *confrontation*. There are instances in which "diseased tissue" is best dealt with in this manner. "Cry aloud, spare not; show my people their transgression."[102] At other times, diseased tissue is best handled by bringing "*comfort*" to the client. "*Comfort, yes, comfort My people! Speak comfort.*".[103] At still other times, therapists must simply withhold what they would like to share with the client simply because the client cannot handle it at that time. "*I still have many things to say to you, but you cannot bear them now.*[104] The most helpful therapists will select from a variety of approaches the approach that best fits the client and the task at hand. The task in this instance is the removal of diseased tissue to discover the growing edge.

CHAPTER NINE

Preventing Psychological Breakdown

POSTULATE 5: A Healthy Brain Maintains Emotional Stability

A 28-yr. old young man of high average intelligence came to see me for career guidance. He left college at the close of his junior year because he was disillusioned about finding a career he would enjoy. After he left college he worked at three different jobs, and did acceptable work in all of them, but he was not very happy about any of them as a career. He felt that he should go back to school and finish a bachelor's degree, but he didn't know what he wanted.

He was emotionally sensitive, overprotected by his mother as he was growing up, kind and tenderhearted, with a special taste for music and the arts. He had thought about a career in music or the fine arts, but felt it would be financially difficult for him.

And besides, he was extremely shy, easily intimidated by strong personalities or crowds. He had a lot of drive, but was tense and easily frustrated. He was liberal in his thinking, willing to experiment, and ready to leave his past behind him.

He was quite resourceful, independent-minded, but emotionally dependent. He was very unstable emotionally, easily annoyed, and easily upset. When upset, tears would come easily.

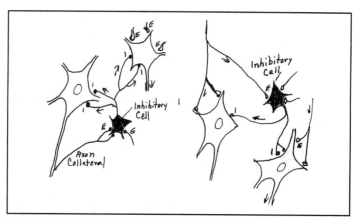

Figure 9.1 Feed-forward and feed-backward circuits.

This was a clear case of a person whose emotional system was not sending appropriate feedback signals to the brain centers that could provide him with the stability that he desperately needed. Heredity contributes quite heavily in this case, —for the statistically minded, 41 percent of the *variance* in this *emotional stability factor* is due to heredity. But other things such as lifestyle, nutrition, and upbringing contribute 59 percent.

This means that a chronically emotionally unstable person must adopt of healthful lifestyle. This means good nutrition, cutting down on sweets to conserve B-vitamins for their nerves, daily physical exercise in the fresh air to sweat out body poisons, and to improve oxygen intake and circulation of nutrients.

It was the American physician Walter B. Cannon who coined the term 'homeostasis" in his book *Wisdom of the Body,* 1932. Cannon set forth the basic

90

idea of feedback as a fundamental physiological principle. He explained that homeostasis is maintained by feedback signals from *what* is needed to *how* that need can be attained. This is an important principle for the guiding of skilled behavior, for making appropriate decisions and for guiding appropriate actions to satisfy our motivational and emotional needs.

Principle: In order for us to maintain emotional stability, our emotional centers must send feedback signals from the needy centers to the brain centers that can meet those needs.

Just as the principle of homeostasis operates in the physical self for the maintenance of a relatively stable internal environment, e.g. body temperature, so this principle operates in the psychological self. Homeostasis in the *psychological* self is its predisposition to maintain stability among contending motivations and other psychodynamic forces.

When the physical body tries to adjust to conditions of extreme heat, for example, the body is adjusting to the stress and discomfort of the heat by perspiring, thereby cooling the body. The process is automatic. It is without conscious intent or effort. To avoid a *calcium deficiency,* as bone tissue detects a diminishing presence of essential calcium, calcium is replenished 'automatically' from the body's calcium storage supply. Those "storage bins" must be supplied from food intake, of course. Another example is *beta-carotene*, a pre-cursor to vitamin A. Beta-carotene is stored and only when vitamin A is needed by the body is beta-carotene converted to vitamin A and drawn upon, thus maintaining physiological homeostasis or stability. Negative feedback signaling the output information to the input storehouses is involved in all these instances.

Likewise, *the healthy psychological self* adjusts homeostatically to prevent extreme departures from a comfortable *internal psychological environment.* Glands and organs throughout the brain and body are constantly supplying appropriate hormones and chemicals to maintain physiological and psychological homeostasis or stability. Flows of neural current trigger the release of appropriate chemicals in just the right amounts. Neuroscience has demonstrated that feedback and feedforward circuitry make homeostasis possible. We have learned that emotional homeostasis is the result of these feedback and feedforward neurological firing patterns. (Figure 9.1)

Principle: Controlled emotional feedback demands a healthy inhibitory circuitry.

POSTULATE 6: Temperance Protects from Psychological Breakdown.

Sometimes translated "self-control," "temperance" [105]typically means the moderate use and practice of anything healthful, and the total abstinence from anything harmful.

Some of us remember our first taste of tobacco—awful! But to be "cool" like the others we wanted to be with, we toughed it out. Eventually the "awful taste" was gone, and we were hooked.

Often we develop a taste for harmful substances by using these at a very young age when our brain nerves are rapidly developing. Our nerves will "adapt" to these harmful substances for a time in order to delay self-destruction. Nevertheless, these harmful substances will take their toll. As the Good Book says, "Whatever a man sows, that he will also reap." [106] The principle is basic.

Parents often have difficulty teaching their children to enjoy certain nourishing foods. Often these parents themselves are "fussy eaters," setting a bad example for their children. Taste buds grow and die every day. Your taste buds can be trained to enjoy virtually any nourishing food. In fact, you don't really taste in your taste buds. Those taste buds are only the receptors that transform the chemical energy into nerve energy that travels to your brain. You taste in your brain! It's amazing how your mind affects your taste. Have you ever reached for a glass of milk fully anticipating the taste of fresh whole milk only to

93

discover that it was buttermilk? Even if you like buttermilk, it just didn't taste good that time! Your mind was thinking fresh milk.

We conducted an experiment in which a group of students were blindfolded. We then asked them to identify the flavors of Jell-O—raspberry, lime, lemon, and orange. Would you believe that they were unable to do so any more than if they guessed without tasting—because they couldn't see the colors! Yet when looking at the colors they were sure they could taste the difference!

On another occasion, when one of our grandsons was about 4 years old, he took a bite of yellow summer squash only to make an awful face spit it out and cry. I turned to the little fellow and said: "That tasted awful, didn't it?" You should have seen the surprised look on his face. To think Grandpa understood! Then I added, "That squash didn't taste good at all, but it has some good things in it to help make your eyes strong and healthy so that you can see real well. Maybe you won't even have to wear glasses like your grandpa has to. Let Grandpa tell you how you can make that awful-tasting squash taste better. Just cut a tiny piece—make sure it is real small so you can barely taste it. If you just eat those tiny pieces, one at a time, it'll begin to taste better and better. But you mustn't take a big piece. Because then it will taste awful!"

His tear-marked eyes looked into mine as he listened intently. Then he tried it. When he cut the first little piece and was about to put it into his mouth, I said, "No, No! That's too big. It must be real tiny!" He put it back on his plate and cut it still smaller. "That's better", I said. Of course, it was so small that he could hardly taste anything. "Now, take a spoonful of something you like from your plate. Then you can try another tiny piece of squash. Make sure it's very small, though," I continued.

The little lad did as he was told and asked, "Is this one all right, Grandpa?" "Yes, that's much better—just a tiny piece." After two or three more such trials, the little fellow said, "It's beginning to taste better already, Grandpa!"

And so it was! He was learning to train his taste buds by small exposures to the distasteful, following each by a rewarding taste, all the while expecting the distasteful to begin tasting good. An important lesson in neural adaptation for all of us! The Creator made our nerves to adapt.

I need to point out that while our mental expectations affect our taste, it is also true that a number of variables such as solubility, concentration, ionization, temperature, and the basic chemical composition of the substance also affect our taste. Furthermore, there appears to be evidence of a genetic link in the transmission of taste preferences for some, though not all people.

Nutritious food should taste delightful! But some of us may need to cut back on the size of our meals as well as the number of calories we take in. Overloading the digestive system, taking in more calories than we consume for normal warmth and energy, takes a heavy toll on our nerves, at first stressing them and later actually destroying them. Our brain nerves are victimized just as surely as the nerves in the rest of our body.

It would help most of us to have a day of fasting every so often, restricting our intake to pure water on that day. If you decide to try this, ease into it by making your last meal before the fasting day a light one. It'll be easier to enjoy the day of fasting! I tried fasting after eating heavily the evening before, and almost passed out by mid-afternoon on the day of fasting! No matter how many times I tried, I just couldn't make it! But when I learned the trick of eating a light supper, I enjoyed my day of fasting, and had plenty of energy to carry out the responsibilities of the day.

More than thirty-two different hormones that affect thought, emotion, and behavior have been found in humans. There may be several hundred. No scientist knows exactly how many there are. At least three hundred seventeen separate kinds of peptides have been recovered from the brain's ventricles!

Among the hormones that are known in the brain or the body, both brain and body produce most of them. They are all present to keep our brain and body in good working order. The ingredients or chemical molecules that make up these hormones and peptides come from the food we eat, the water that we drink, the sunshine and fresh air that we take into our systems. Our habits of exercise and rest determine how well we utilize their benefits. So try to be temperate in your eating habits, your exercise, your periods of rest, your intake of fresh air and sunshine and fresh water to protect yourself from emotional breakdown.

While writing this book I received a phone call from a dedicated, conscientious hard-working woman whose nerves were shattered. As she related her mental confusion, her uncontrollable crying spells, her inability to make a simple decision, her overpowering apprehensiveness over what this would all mean for her future, she pleaded in desperation, "What shall I do?"

Obviously she was on the brink of a complete nervous breakdown. She was a brilliant, healthy, energetic, and motivated person. Usually balanced in judgment, and conscientious about dependability, she was feeling these qualities suddenly falling apart.

She was well aware of her need for a temperate lifestyle. As she put it in a later visit, "I know what I'm supposed to do, but I didn't see how I could with all that needed to get done."

She was a new face on a new assignment with pressing deadlines to meet important vacancies to fill, and threatening group conflicts to resolve. So she climaxed a little more than two months of little sleep and irregular "catch it on the run" meals, by working around the clock without food or sleep for the better part of the weekend just before she phoned me.

It is interesting how we who love our work can so easily forget to be temperate. I remember when I used to hold nightly meeting evangelistic crusades all year long, every year, visiting up to forty homes a day. In the midst of all of that one day, my wife asked me, "Honey, what are you leaving for the Lord to do?" A good question!

Intemperate stimulation or deprivation, intemperate rewards or punishments, obsessive rehearsals, compulsive rituals, fanatical pursuits of all kinds, "all work and no play" or vice-versa, and intemperance of all kinds prevent the development of true psychological health. They stress the brain and body efforts to maintain harmony in the chemical secretions that flow in and out of nerve, gland, and organ.

In addition, extremes push the brain to set up new reference standards for "typical" or "regular" operations. In other words, in an attempt to handle the extreme situation, the new reference standards will become the "norm" for the brain. In the future, the person will tend to depend upon extremes to avoid boredom in life.

Any enjoyment and satisfaction coming from intemperance are only for moments in the stream of life. Besides, they lack the high quality, depth, fullness, and abundance of joy, peace, satisfaction and true deep-seated excitement that characterize a life of temperance. Furthermore, intemperance continues to break down the health of the brain.

On the other hand, temperate stimulation and activity in balance contributes best to psychological health. Temperance protects against mental or emotional breakdown. Such persons find satisfaction in the typical experiences in everyday life. A positive outlook and peace and calm are more natural to come by.

Many of the hormones produced in the brain travel down into the body by means of both blood vessels and hollow nerves. Many hormones produced in the brain are also produced in many glands and organs of the body. They affect our thinking, our emotions, our behavior, and our body functions. Body and mind are intimately related. Each affects the other.

In brain-to-body gland relationships the controlling messages from the brain get stronger as they move down from the brain through a hierarchy of glands. Each message lasts longer, travels further and affects greater numbers of other organs. The permeable capillaries, present in all of the endocrine glands except the testes and the brain, allow these chemicals to leak out of these glands into the bloodstream, travel in the bloodstream and then leave the bloodstream to enter some other gland. With this passage of chemicals from brain to body, it is easy to see how the brain can affect the body.

The blood-brain barrier prevents *most* but *not all* hormones from moving in the other direction—i.e., *from the body* glands and organs *into the brain.* Steroids are examples of hormones that do pass readily from the body into the brain. Evidence is mounting showing that the blood-brain barrier is like an active pump selectively allowing some and preventing other chemicals from passing from the body into the brain.

Is it possible that imbalances of nutrition and the ingestion of drugs can upset the balance of chemicals in body and brain to the detriment of psychological functioning? I cannot imagine how it could be otherwise. Is it possible that persistent inappropriate thinking styles can upset the balance of chemicals in body and brain to the detriment of psychological functioning? I think so. Is it possible that excessively high or low emotional experiences can upset the balance of chemicals in both body and brain to the detriment of psychological functioning? I think so. The overwhelming evidence of science today is that the brain and body interact with amazing intimacy. The more that we discover about both, the more we become aware of the power of their interaction. And every discovery we make raises more intriguing questions.

As noted earlier, there are times when alleviating a distracting symptom with a drug may provide sufficient temporary relief to facilitate a truly healing therapy without the continuing use of drugs. Even so, science is not able to tell us all that the drug will do in a given human being. There are probably many more harmful side effects than are known not the least of which can easily be an overload at the receptor sites of many organs or nerves.

Addiction to opiate drugs of any kind—for example, to heroin—is determined by the interactions of hormones and their brain receptors. Many kinds of brain cells have opiate receptors. The brain secretes its own opiate-like drugs that are received into certain brain cells so that the brain can treat itself during emergencies. Why would a person become dangerously addicted to a drug that his own brain secretes? An accepted view in science is that injections of external opiates turn off the brain factories that produce the brain's own opiates because the brain senses that enough brain opiates are already present. The addiction, scientists believe, arises from this shutdown of the internal brain factory. The addict feels driven to seek for more opiates. But as long as addicts continue to receive external opiates the addiction will remain. When addicts are not receiving external opiates for a sufficient period of time—long enough for the brain to realize it has need of some opiates to prepare for emergencies—the brain will resume the production of its own opiate-like hormones. Only then will the addiction cease. During the emergency, just the right amount of opiate is secreted to care for the emergency. This is all accomplished by the interplay of the excitatory and inhibitory pathways we talked about earlier. When kept healthy, these pathways are marvelously precise in the delivery of their coded messages and their chemical secretions. The right amount in the right place at the right time. A mind-boggling wonder of the Creator's handiwork!

There are evidences that diseases of the brain and mind may be caused by the excessive secretion or the diminished secretion of hormones in the brain itself, even as endocrine disorders of the body have been correlated with excessive or diminished secretions of hormones. The interrelationship between chemical and behavioral actions in the body and the brain is complex but real. From what is known today it appears that what happens chemically in the brain more strongly affects what happens in the body than previously thought.

The point is that hormones and other chemicals do influence thought, emotion, and behavior. These may be triggered for release in the *brain* or in the *body*. They flow through *nerves* and *blood vessels*. A given hormone can influence several human experiences. For example, *vasopressin* might influence memory, thirst, satiation, addiction, rage, fear, and pain. Any *one* of these experiences might also be influenced by *a harmony of several* hormones. For example, *pain* might call for the secretion of a balanced group of hormones. Fear, like rage, releases *catecholamines* and many other hormones including *endorphin, prolactin, and vasopressin.* Some of these hormones are secreted in the digestive tract, increasing gastric and intestinal disturbances and bowel incontinence. Most of us recall having these experiences when we have been especially fearful.[107]

We all know how difficult it is to change a self-destructive lifestyle. Entrenched debilitating habits and the indulgence of harmful drugs or drinks are most difficult to stop. While each of us is different and may need a different approach, we need to have a kindly, positive regard toward ourselves. We need to remind ourselves that we were created in God's own image, and with a brain designed for infinite development and abundant joy. If we know that we are following a self-destructive lifestyle, we need to ask ourselves if we *really* want to continue that lifestyle. Are we ready to move in a new direction? Are we ready to follow our best judgment?

People are different. Some may need to be *temperate* in their moves for change. They may need to taper off on their bad habits. And they may need to replace these with the opposite "good" habits. Having decided upon their ultimate goals, they may need to plan on small, successive, and increasing approximations to those ultimate goals. The nerves of the brain and body will adapt, and will respond to *moderate* stimulations to form new habits. A few people may be able to make a precipitous break with the past, displacing it with major new beginnings in their lifestyle. This depends on how major the changes are that need to be made, and upon the physical and psychological profile of the person that needs to change. Regardless, do it "heartily" and "joyously", knowing that you are doing what you really want to do.

However, remember that extreme stimulations, *even when intended to produce healthy changes in nerve and nerve patterns of response* will only result in shutting down the very pathways that needed to adapt. Neuroscientists are familiar with the function of the relatively refractory and the absolutely refractory thresholds of nerve pathways. These thresholds are designed to protect the nerve cell from breakdown under conditions of extreme stimulation. As noted earlier, however, there is a limit to the stress-load these mortal nerves can handle.

Aside from breakdown, nerve pathways and nerve clusters lose their positive potential effectiveness by chemical imbalances, and unhealthy synaptic changes. Furthermore, to disturb or disrupt the circulation of the electric currents in the nervous system or their chemical secretions may reduce the strength of the vital powers and deaden the responsiveness of the mind.

Disruption of healthy functioning in any one part of mind or body affects the health of the entire mind and body. *Intemperance of any kind* works *toward* weakening and destroying both mind and body.

103

POSTULATE 7: Psychological addictions cause the brakes of your brain to fail

"Marijuana never hurt anybody!"

I saw a true believer in 19-yr.-old Erik Samuelson. Seated in the black leather easy chair in my office, he meant every word. "In fact," he continued, "alcohol is a lot worse for a fellow than marijuana. And don't forget there're some brainy people who use the stuff, like schoolteachers and some of you psychologists. Well, maybe not you, but I read about some who do."

Even though I smiled at his brashness in the defense of marijuana, I knew he was right—at least partly! There are a lot of people, young and old, and some of them with Ph.D.'s, who use and encourage others to use marijuana.

But I was not convinced. Not even by what Chad Whitener, another young marijuana user, told me about his own experience.

"I smoke marijuana every day just like cigarettes and it hasn't hurt me. It makes me feel good. My girl friend, Ann, uses it too, and if she didn't she'd blow her mind with all the stuff she's been through. Her father raped her and kicked her out of the house. Marijuana really helps her instead of hurting her!"

I could see his point. Ann surely needed *something* to help her through her own private hell! And what these two teen-agers told me goes right along with what scores of other users have told me: marijuana produces a mild "high" that feels good, it isn't as habit-forming as cigarettes, and, contrary to a lot of talk by those who haven't tried it, the users don't always get bored with the mild highs and move on to hard drugs such as heroin.

But I'm still afraid of marijuana. And one of the reasons I'm afraid is that marijuana users often develop a "psychological addiction".

What is a psychological addiction?

Many drug users know that there are basically two kinds of addiction that come with using certain chemicals: psychological and physiological. (Careful now, that's two different words even though they look alike at first glance.)

Mention drug addiction, and most people think of the physiological addiction such as may be caused by the use of tobacco and heroin, —the body comes to depend upon having the chemical in the system in order to operate. When the user tries to quit using the drug, his body rebels with various kinds of pains and extremely unpleasant reactions which make him feel that he just has to have the drug in order to survive. Marijuana, LSD, and some other drugs do not act that way. They are not physiologically addicting.

Psychological addiction on the other hand often takes a firm hold on the emotions and the personality of a user causing him to become almost as dependent upon the drug as if he had a physiological addiction. Ann is an example of a person who has become dependent upon marijuana, because it seems to make her tormenting memories go away for awhile. The only trouble is, that when the effects of the drug have worn off, the problems all come back, and she needs more of the drug.

But is psychological addiction all that bad? If it makes her problems go away for awhile, why not use it?

Unfortunately, while those problems are going away, other problems come sneaking in. Mary was just 16 when she told me, "You're going to hate me when you learn what I did—are you going to be mad at me? It's something I told you that I would never do—do you know Joe Embry? Well anyway, I might as well tell you—we went all the way. You're mad at me, aren't you?"

"No", I replied, 'but had you known him before, Mary?"

"No, but he was really nice to me. I wish I hadn't now. But at the time I knew what I was doing, but I really didn't mind."

And then I became suspicious. I knew Mary as a girl of principles, and it was not like her to have her conscience salved so easily. But I didn't have to wonder long.

"He gave me some grass. He told me that I didn't have to take it if I didn't want to, but that it wouldn't hurt me because he'd been using it all the time. So we really had a good time. It made me feel good. Only I wish I hadn't done the other. You know I'm not that kind of girl. You're not mad at me, are you?"

I wasn't mad at Mary, but I was surely furious at that drug that had short-circuited her conscience when she needed it most.

Like a car that has been driven through deep water and has almost no braking power until the brakes dry out, the person on a marijuana-induced high finds it almost impossible to say "No" to something which he would usually refuse very easily. Mary's emotional brakes failed to stop at sex with a guy she hardly knew. Others find themselves careening into other more dangerous drugs while their brakes are out. And the regrets come later in years of binding physiological addiction or seriously damaged minds, or even suicide.

Another serious problem with marijuana use was brought to light by Dr. Morton A. Stenchever of the University of Utah Medical Center in Salt Lake City. He tested 49 marijuana users and 20 control subjects who had not used any drugs or medications for the preceding six months. While those who were not using drugs were found to have the normal average of 1.2% of their reproductive cells with broken chromosomes, those using marijuana had more than twice as many, an average of 3.4% with broken chromosomes. Dr. Stenchever suggested that this could mean that marijuana may be related to birth defects and cancer. If this is true, the chances of marijuana users having deformed children would be over 200% more than nonmarijuana users!

As if this damaging evidence against the use of marijuana were not enough, other studies in the field of long-term memory and habit seem to suggest that any often-repeated act or thought may actually be making permanent chemical and physical changes in the body. This process may well be why many marijuana users find that they continue to use the drug long after they realize that they really don't need or want it.

Our brain, nervous system, glands, and organs perform all of our psychological functioning. *Inhibitory* pathways continually restrain the *excitatory* pathways in our brain, and in the rest of our nervous system. The hallmark of a healthy mind is a healthy *inhibitory* system. Without a healthy *inhibitory* system we could not guide or control our physical movements. Neither could we guide or control our thoughts or emotions.

Scientists have been studying for sometime various ways in which the effects of the neural *inhibitory* system might be used to slow down *excitatory* brain systems like the norepinephrine system that might be exciting anxiety. They have tried enhancing the effect of GABA, an inhibitory chemical secreted by inhibitory pathways.

Researchers have found a receptor site especially receptive to chemical messages given by antianxiety drugs. They called this site the "benzodiazepine receptor," a site receptive to antianxiety drugs that include Valium and Librium. It is now known that these sites are widely distributed throughout the cerebral cortex. Furthermore, both GABA and benzodiazepine receptors tend to be located close to one another on neurons, possibly facilitating one another.

As understanding of the *inhibitory* and *excitatory* systems continues to develop, researchers are hopeful that we will truly understand the important human emotion labeled "anxiety" in terms of the chemical processes occurring in the brain.

The use of ill-chosen drugs, the overtaxing of our nervous system, unbalanced dietary habits, inadequate physical exercise or excessive physical exertion all contribute to stressing or disrupting the balanced operation of this pair of intercepts throughout the nervous system. Physical, mental, or emotional fatigue typically causes the "brakes" or the inhibitory system to fail when needed. Self-denial when needed requires a healthy inhibitory system. In fact, one cannot resist ingesting harmful drugs or foods without it.

While it is not always easy to separate fact from fiction in perusing the advertising targeting our habits of nutrition, research has shown us that our body and brain condition *is* a reflection of what we eat.

Caffeine is just one example of the widespread danger associated with common dietary habits. The coffee break is as American as apple pie, and hundreds of thousands of cups of coffee are probably consumed daily in America. Additional sources of caffeine intake are tea, cola drinks, and cocoa. Coffee as used contains the most caffeine—100 to 150 milligrams per cup. While tea leaves contain more caffeine than coffee beans, prepared tea has a lower concentration of caffeine—about 90 milligrams per six-ounce cup. A 12 ounce bottle of Coca-Cola contains about 55 milligrams of caffeine, and a six-ounce cup of cocoa contains about 50 milligrams of caffeine. According to some authorities, caffeine causes hyperactivity and insomnia in children. Large quantities of caffeine produce low-grade fever, irritability, and abnormal rhythms of the heart called arrhythmia. Researchers at Harvard School of Public Health found that heavy coffee drinkers were more likely to have cancer of the lower urinary tract.

Caffeine consumption is just one example of the many dietary habits that pose threats to our health. A good rule of thumb for a healthy diet is to select carefully the foods we eat, and eat moderately.

In the case described under **Postulate 1,** the patient had only to break her addiction to soft drinks, which she consumed, by the case every few days. This was fortunate because, as her husband had informed me, he was about out of funds for her treatment, having already spent thousands on psychiatrists to try to get her well. Her nerves could not recover their health as long as she was consuming so much sugar and caffeine. Her diet otherwise was surprisingly healthful and in fair balance. This was surprising, because typically a sugar-addiction perverts the appetite.

Generally speaking, the *unperverted* appetite can depend on "tissue hunger" dictating their tastes for the foods containing the appropriate nutrients. One study with 2-3 yr. old infants showed that infants could select a balanced diet by themselves if there was no refined sugar in any of their food![108]

In another study, two scientists demonstrated that food intake tends to vary with changes in bodily needs for a particular substance. Rats deprived of their adrenal glands drank much heavier salt solutions than rats that had intact functioning adrenal glands.[109]

111

I repeated this study, adding a sugar solution to the options available to the rats. I discovered that even though the adrenalectomized rats initially showed a distinct preference for the salt solution needed for survival, after a few samplings of the sugar solution, they neglected the essential salt solution and showed their preference for the sugar solution. Even though, without their adrenal glands, they needed the salt solution to survive! Sugar can apparently pervert the appetite even when your life is at stake![110]

Unfortunately, sometimes our imperfect bodies send us appetite signals of genuine tissue hunger that appear to be a perverted hunger, when in fact a defective gland or organ may be signaling the need for a nutrient in unusual amount.

The following case sadly illustrates this reason for "tissue hunger". A three-year-old boy hated anything sweet but craved anything salty. He not only licked the salt off the crackers and other foods, but on one occasion he climbed onto the kitchen counter to procure the salt shaker put "out of reach" by his concerned parents, and was observed to consume nearly the entire contents of the salt shaker! Ultimately his parents were putting an excessive amount of salt on his food simply to get him to eat his food!

The parents finally brought him to the hospital for other problems. On the well-regulated diet of the hospital, the three-year-old died within a week! An autopsy showed that his adrenal glands were defective. This defect had caused his body to lose salt faster than it was possible to replace on a normal diet.[111]

When the nerves are robbed of their needed nutrition, the balancing of the inhibitory and excitatory pathways of the nervous system is disrupted. Psychological health cannot then be achieved. Anyone dealing with nerve disorders knows how long it takes for nerves to heal. There are no quick fixes for shattered nerves! Let's go beyond merely treating symptoms. Let's try to help our nerves to experience true healing. Every little effort helps!

LEFT HEMISPHERE
(Right Side of Body)

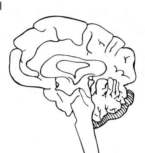

Speech/Verbal

Logical, Mathematical

Linear, Detailed

Sequential

Controlled

Intellectual

Dominant

Worldly

Active

Analytic

Reading

Writing

Naming Sequential
Ordering

Perception of
Significant Order

Complex
Motor Sequences

RIGHT HEMISPHERE
(Left Side of Body)

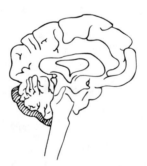

Spatial/Musical

Holistic

Artistic, Symbolic

Simultaneous

Emotional

Intuitive, Creative

Minor (Quiet)

Spiritual

Receptive

Synthetic, Gestalt

Facial Recognition

Simultaneous
Comprehension

Perception of
Abstract Patterns

Recognition of
Complex Figures

114

POSTULATE 8: Distributing the workload of your brain protects it from breakdown

We have two brains: a left and a right. Both are chemically and structurally different. Modern brain scientists tell us that our left brain is our expressive brain—using letters, words, and numbers. It analyzes, organizes, and expresses itself. Our right brain is our receptive brain—receiving patterns, pictures, complex wholes, dreams, visions, aspirations, and intuitions. It sees the whole picture and doesn't try to analyze it. Women's intuitions emerge there. That's why they can't give you any "reasons" for their intuitions! Some have said that the right brain doesn't read, write, or do arithmetic! I'm not so sure about the reading! While true for most readers, I suspect that speed learners who read concepts and ideas rather than words and the letters that make up the words are using their right brain! And high-speed mathematicians seem to see patterns and wholes rather than individual numbers! Some have called the right brain our *mystic* brain, since its wisdom comes from some mystical source, probably from the unseen cosmos. How we receive its wisdom determines our spirituality.

For some people it is more natural to use their left brain. Reductionist scientists and critical thinking theologians are often among these. They dissect, analyze, categorize, rearrange or reassemble the parts. They examine different ways in which the parts may fit together and try to determine the whole from a collection of the parts.

Others are more inclined to use their right brain. They learn by "soaking it in"—by receiving—by meditation, by an openness to hear "that still small voice" that says "this is the way, walk in it." Like the psalmist they pray, "Open my eyes, that I may see wondrous things in Your law." They are emotionally moved deeply by the rich variety of patterns in music and in nature. They hear what left-brain people do not hear. They see what left-brain people do not see.

Our genetic code may have programmed the richness of development in certain areas of our brain, providing us with certain natural talents. It is natural to pursue that which comes easiest. By working to develop a talent we do not naturally possess, we stimulate the growth and development of new areas of the brain. In this way, we can "acquire" a talent we did not have. God created us all to multiply the talents He has given us.[112] If we all worked to develop a facility in the use of both brains, we would be less likely to overwork any one area of the brain to the neglect of many other areas.

Fatigue is a signal for changing our particular activity. Mental fatigue usually disappears with a little physical exercise activating the brain's motor strip and its pathways. Or it may disappear with a shift in the *kind* of mental activity engaged in. For example, number crunching interspersed with music or art.

Many people pursue a very narrow range of activities. Many carry their work with them wherever they go. This work places heavy demands on a limited area of their brain. The result will be an imbalance in the secretion of the hormones and chemicals needed for healthy brain functioning.

116

The balanced use of our brain is vital for mental and emotional health. We need to practice exercises requiring the use of little used areas of the brain. By establishing a hierarchy of exercises, and beginning with the easiest until each becomes natural, we are more easily motivated to develop balance in the use of the mental powers.

CHAPTER TEN

Nurturing the Healing Process

POSTULATE 9: The Reactance Principle awakens the brain to truth

A wife and her husband came for marriage counseling. It was obvious that she was angry. *She* had set up the session, and 'dragged him in'. He sat silent, meekly listening as his wife 'tore him apart' with her long list of complaints.

At the close of the session, I suggested that both of them return the next week with a personal list of all the good things that they could think of about their partner. I urged them to make the list as long as they could, and to bring their lists to the next session.

In the next session, the husband handed me his list. I was amazed! He had a whole page of good things about his wife! After hearing *her* the week before, I doubted that he could come up with *anything* good about her. Then I turned to his wife.

"And your list?" I asked.

"I didn't make any ", she said.

"Oh, you probably didn't have time?" I asked.

"Oh, no, I had time, but I couldn't think of *anything* good about him. Doctor, you don't understand. My husband is really bad!"

And she proceeded to rehearse some of the terrible things she had listed the week before.

At this point I interrupted her, and finished rehearsing the list she had given me the week before to reassure her that I *did* remember. (I had reviewed my notes in preparation for this session!) Then I added (remembering that she *loved* to study her Bible):

"In fact, as I was thinking about the things you told me about your husband, I was convinced that the prophet Isaiah described him perfectly in his first chapter when he said he is 'rotten, from the crown of his head to the soles of his feet...there is not one good thing in him!'

"Oh, he's not *that* bad!" she said, and then began to tell me one good thing about him, and then another, and still another.

That wife's last remark brought to the surface of her mind the *good* side of her husband. It was the *reactance principle* at work when she was confronted with her extreme position. As long as she kept her recognition of that good side of him buried beneath her consciousness, she would only see him as bad, and treat him that way! *At the same time, she would be expressing the worst side of herself in anger, frustration, anxiety, and even depression over what would seem to her as a "hopeless" situation!*

It is natural for us to see our situation as extreme. This defends our extreme emotions, our rash words and reckless actions. In fact, split brain studies show that we have a remarkable way of justifying or rationalizing our careless words or actions! Psychologist Michael Gazzaniga believes that this easily happens because, as he sees it, the brain has a modular organization. He believes the brain is organized into somewhat independent units that work on the same problem. According to his theory, the brain tends to by-pass those modules that contain the truth that contradicts our actions! When these "truth modules" are by-passed we are not aware of the whole truth! Furthermore, Leon Festinger's *cognitive dissonance* theory had previously led to studies testing Festinger's theory. These *cognitive dissonance* studies found that indeed the brain doesn't like *dissonance*. The brain doesn't like it when our actions don't match our beliefs! And listen to this! These studies have found that if our actions continue to contradict our beliefs, we will change our beliefs to match our actions, —not our actions to match our beliefs! In the meantime, according to Gazzaniga, the brain simply by-passes the modules that would show up our dysfunctional words and actions! If this is true, it would explain why we do not even recognize our own dysfunctionality!

If we find ourselves acting in such a dysfunctional manner, it is often helpful to write a letter to the offending person, read it over, talk to the Lord about it, and throw it away. Or re-write it to express our perceptions more accurately. It is easier for us to recognize how extreme our position is when we write it down, and re-read it. Remember, when we act as though life for us is all bad, our brain is probably by-passing the truth modules to make our beliefs match our actions!

POSTULATE 10: Awakening the Traces of a Divine Creation Brings Healing[113]

We will often find a new outlook on life by tapping into one or more of these Divine traces. Too many people look at themselves and others through dark glasses. They have learned to be "helpless". They have been trapped by despair, repeated delinquent acts, uncontrollable tempers, prolonged feelings of bitterness. They have the "loser's syndrome".

A war is raging within -- the war between the desire for goodness and the inclination to badness, between the perception of right and the perceived attractiveness of wrong. This creates an internal restlessness, confusion, and neurotic conflicts.

We need to explore the likely outcomes of following the options available on both sides in "the war that rages within", and encourage the nurturing of the better self! We may need to take a walk, breathe deeply, and crystallize what our best self would do if we gave it some support.

Many even religious persons make life miserable for themselves by chastising themselves for their shortcomings. We need to remove our dark glasses and find the good that the Divine Creator has put in every one of us.

We each possess intellectual power, spiritual power, the ability to know what is right, the desire for goodness, and our unique combinations of individualistic and positive qualities We need to acknowledge the Source of these qualities and thank a loving God for creating these within us!

The nurturing of our impatience for whatever 'feels' good is an encouragement to emotional immaturity -- the level that every child would operate on, namely the immediate gratification of the senses. These are precursors to the development of anti-social personalities.[114] Followed in early childhood, this practice of doing what initially feels good has been highly correlated with the development of children without a conscience.[115]

Better to encourage ourselves to follow through on our deepest desires for goodness, doing the right thing, and nurturing our spiritual power. We will soon experience "good feelings" that are not transient, but enduring. Thank God for these good feelings and for the privilege of fellowship with Him. I have found God quick to respond and energize those positive gifts He has blessed us with. These positive resources, i.e. desires for goodness, perception of right and spiritual power, will continue to increase and then multiply. They will gain new positive resources. They will be making long strides in the journey toward genuine mental and emotional health.

POSTULATE 11: The Sandwich Principle inspires hope.

It's like taking a sugar coated pill!

This technique can be used by any caring counselor, parent, or friend who wants to instill hope in one that is burdened with a sense of guilt. You can use it on yourself by talking to yourself. You can use it in your private prayers.

The sandwich technique begins and ends with hope engendering statements. The acknowledgement of the problem is sandwiched in between. By packaging our problem in this way, we acknowledge and confess it, and more readily move on with our life in hope. We feel no need to deny it. When people do it with us, they inspire us with hope. When we do it in prayer we are inspired with hope.

The prayer that Jesus taught His disciples and us to pray, commonly referred to as "The Lord's Prayer" teaches us to do this when we come to Him. In that prayer we are taught to begin with the positive acknowledgement of His holiness and our desire for Him to rule in our lives. It is then that we confess our sins. Then we close with an extolling of His Kingdom, His Power, and His Glory! That kind of praying for forgiveness places the focus of our brain on God's righteousness, love, and all-powerfulness. It lifts the soul inspiring us with hope.

Jesus further demonstrated this sandwiching principle in his session with the Samaritan woman at the well. He sandwiched his mention of her destructive

125

lifestyle between genuine commendations for her honesty! And he didn't condemn or fault her for her destructive lifestyle! [116]

This principle inspires hope in anyone. Try it when you want to inspire hope in someone who feels they are a failure. It reminds them of their positive qualities. It inspires them to build on those positive qualities. This inspiration is motivating.

Principle: The brain remembers the first and last statements best, and more easily forgets the statements near

This kind of simple sandwich technique doesn't try to deny any failure. But it places the negative between two positives. This serial order emphasizes the positive and minimizes the negative. Our minds or another person's mind will more easily recall the positive qualities. After all, the positive qualities took the first and last place in the mind. Likewise, the sandwiched negative aspect(s) of the experience will be weakened in its power to control us. Instead, the positive aspects can be better mobilized and built upon to promote psychological growth.

Our "desire for goodness" is more easily strengthened when some of the goodness we do possess has been uncovered and recognized. This discovery is a powerful motivator toward growth.

While teaching at the seminary, one student who couldn't stand my lecture raised his hand and blurted out: "Dr. Chalmers, I think you are too complimentary about man! Man is totally depraved! There is no good thing in him!" Later, he came to my office to apologize for his outrage, and said: "I have been thinking about what I said in our last class period, and about your lecture. I reflected upon my own ministry, and realized that I have not had any success in bringing people to Christ. And the Lord has used you to bring thousands to Him. I have decided that my attitude toward sinners may be the reason. I need to recognize whatever goodness God has put in them, and encourage them to nurture it."

God has put some of His goodness into every person, and into everything He has made. Our common enemy, Satan, the fallen angel once named "Lucifer" or "Son of the Morning", has tried to obliterate every trace of that image of God found in the works of God's creation. But he has not succeeded. Look at the beauty of nature, renewed every spring—the promise of the Resurrection. Look at the remarkable displays of fearless courage and love that drives people to risk their lives to save others! Every time you find such heaven-sent virtues displayed, you are seeing traces of the Divine image. If we would look for the traces of the image of God in people and in nature all about us, we would become better acquainted with God![117] He is wonderfully kind and loving.

The Bible does *not* teach that a person must repent *before* he comes to Christ.[118]Every desire for truth and purity, every conviction of our own sinfulness, is evidence that His Spirit is moving upon our hearts. It is true that in our sin-prone nature, without Divine power from above working within us, there is no possibility of deliverance from evil.

127

Without Christ, we cannot do anything![119] With Him
we can do anything![120]

CHAPTER ELEVEN

A Powerful Trio That Heals: Faith, Hope, and Love

"Through the powerful influence of faith, hope, and love, the psychiatrist or teacher can accomplish wonders in the treatment of the person. Without these three potent ingredients his medicine is unprofitably flat." Dorsey[121]

POSTULATE 12: Hope stimulates psychological growth.

I recall that before I pursued my doctorate in psychology, I had my first class in Pastoral Counseling at the seminary. The guest professor was a practicing clinical psychologist. In his closing remarks in one class period he said, "Whatever you do in the counseling session, always be sure that you inspire your client with hope. Never leave that to chance. Make **sure** that you have inspired your client with hope."[122] I have thought of that professor's counsel many, many times, as I have witnessed the struggles of my patients.

Modern science is finding that hope is more than the desire or even expectation that something future will turn out all right. University of Kansas psychologist C. R. Snyder[123] compared the academic achievement of students high and low on hope. He found that hope was a better predictor of academic achievement than were their scores on the SAT, highly correlated with I.Q. and used as a predictor for college performance. Snyder also found that people with high levels of hope are able to motivate themselves. They feel that they will find ways to reach their goals. They are flexible in their ways of reaching their goals and in their readiness to switch goals if the one they originally set becomes impossible. When they are in difficulty they reassure themselves that things will get better. They are astute enough to break down enormous tasks into smaller, manageable pieces.

Clinical experience has shown that if someone can be inspired with hope, that person will not give in to overwhelming anxiety, a defeatist attitude, or even depression in the face of tragic disappointments. Studies have shown that hopeful people have less depression, are less anxious, and have fewer emotional distresses.

Related and contributing to hope is the temperament shyness vs. boldness. The bold are more readily hopeful. The shy are more prone to feeling stress, to caution, doubt, and despair. Research has shown that the timid or shy person is prone to schizoid disorders, tuberculosis, ulcers, etc.[124]

Jerome Kagan, developmental psychologist from Harvard, believes that temperamental timidity and boldness are biologically determined. The *amygdala* and its circuitry appear to be involved. He noticed the similarity between the temperament of cats and the temperament of infants and toddlers. In timid infants and toddlers the *amygdala* is unusually excitable, whereas the amygdala is not as easily

130

excited among the bold infants.[125] Earlier, from his research on humans, Raymond Cattell hypothesized that shyness and boldness are built in from birth. He noticed that the sympathetic branch of the autonomic nervous system reacts much more readily in shy people than in the socially bold.[126]

In my clinical practice I have found that constitutionally or genetically determined temperaments can be changed. Through a series of hope-instilling habit-pattern-replacement strategies, shyness has ceased to be experienced physiologically as well as behaviorally in numerous patients. Endogenous depressives have experienced freedom from depression. Lesbians and homosexuals have experienced a complete reversal to their normally expected sex role. In addition, numerous other cases in which the problems were shown by identical-twin studies to be heavily genetically influenced have also experienced an eradication of the problem. In all of these cases, penetrating psychological testing and real-life data have confirmed the changes reported.[127]

Temperament is not destiny. People do not have to be stuck with the way they were born! About one in three infants who come into the world with all the signs of an over-excitable *amygdala* have lost their timidity by the time they reach kindergarten.[128]

Hope mobilizes a person's energies and brings focus to a person's behavior. Personal triumph and fulfillment is experienced vicariously before the fact. Hope provides the assurance of something positive and rewarding. Hope stabilizes the emotions and the thinking, as well as the behaviors. Hope is an anchor for the innermost self.

We need to inspire others with hope. This means that *we* must have a positive outlook on life. A positive aura as real as the magnetic field (which science still doesn't understand) surrounds the person that is full of hope. This "hope field" surrounding us will spread to others. Without hope, there is no motivation for psychological growth. There is little chance for healing.

POSTULATE 13: Faith reduces stress and promotes healing.

There are perceptions of threat, both real and imagined, that when modified, remove the stress load upon both the psychological and physiological self. The accounts of the four Hebrews, Daniel, Hananiah, Mishael, and Azariah, detailed in the first four chapters of the Bible book of *Daniel*, demonstrate this fact. These men placed their highest values of fidelity to their Creator above everything else in life. They trusted this Highest Power to supply them with the necessary grace to weather the consequences imposed by the king of Babylon. Consequently, this real threat to their lives was met with an undisturbed peace of mind.

When I was asked to assist the survivors of Hurricane Andrew to successfully cope with post-traumatic-stress disorders, the powerful effects of faith and consequent perception upon these survivors became strikingly evident.

In one case, a mother who gave birth to a baby one month after the hurricane struck, was treated for the PTSD she had experienced. At the same time her baby, then almost six months old, appeared "frozen with fear". She did not make any sounds, cry, reach for food, or perform any of the behaviors of a healthy six-month old. The perceptions of the mother had apparently translated into prenatal physiological stress.

In contrast, another mother surviving Hurricane Andrew came to have her children checked for PTSD. Following a thorough evaluation, it was clear that she had not suffered from the ordeal. She only wanted to be sure her children had not. She recounted the experience:

"We had gone to bed after hearing the weather report that the Hurricane had shifted course and would not be coming our way. About 2 a. m. I was awakened by the storm hitting the house, as were my two children who were sleeping upstairs. They hurried downstairs and we went to the hallway of our small home. Our baby was fast asleep. I debated for a few seconds as to whether to disturb her sleep, and then decided to move her to the hallway with the rest of us. No sooner had I lifted her from her bed than a huge spike flew through the window and landed on the pillow right where her head had been seconds before! I thanked God for sparing her!

"Then with my two older children in the hallway, we talked about how good God had been to us all through our life, protecting us in so many previous instances, and providing us with all our needs and so many extra blessings. We talked of how God might not choose to let us live until morning this time. I suggested that the two children and I would pray for Daddy (who was out of the State on business), so that when he came back, if he found that he had no children and no 'mommy', he would not lose faith in God. The two older children joined me in that prayer.

"As it happened, though part of the roof was torn off, several of the windows were blown open, and a whole section of the house torn apart, we were spared! None of us were injured physically. But I did want my children checked for post-traumatic stress disorder."

In spite of a thorough evaluation of the children, I could not find any evidence of a stress disorder! I was witnessing a modern account of the ancient lines:

"You will keep him in perfect peace,
Whose mind is stayed *on You,*
Because he trusts in You." [129]

A trust that molds and fashions our perceptions can make a profound psychological and physiological impact.

Real life studies out of Harvard Medical Clinic and the University of Texas Health Science Center in Dallas have demonstrated remarkably that the white cell count rises dramatically and the immunizing hormones secreted within the body are greatly increased whenever the patient exercises faith. The contrary effect follows whenever doubt and negative thinking sets in.[130]

Freud (1953, p. 289) once said "Expectation colored by hope and faith is an effective force with which we have to reckon in *all* our attempts at treatment and cure."

One of the methods used to investigate the effects of a patient's expectations in a doctor-patient relationship is for the doctor to administer a pharmacologically inert medication, commonly known as a *placebo*. In spite of the inert nature of the medication, dramatic pharmacological effects result. Such placebos have been reported to account for healing in from 30 to 70% of the cases tested, even for repair of tissue damage! According to J. D. Frank, the beneficial effects of the placebo lie in its symbolic power: "It gains its potency through being a tangible symbol of the physician's role as healer. In our society, the physician validates his power by prescribing medication, just as a shaman in a primitive tribe may validate his by spitting out a bit of bloodstained down at the proper moment." [131] In one sense, then, the expectation is colored by a faith in the physician as a healer.

The placebo effect can affect every system and cell in the body, determine what hormones and chemicals will be secreted and where, and bring about profound healing. With such outcomes, one cannot dismiss the power of a patient's expectations or faith. As psychiatrist William Sadler put it: "Faith calls for a complete and unconditional surrender of one's whole body, mind, and spirit to the idea which is believed in. Of necessity, it must further include obedience to that which it accepts." [132]

The examples cited above point to the power of a person's expectancy or faith to bring about chemical, tissue, and other physiological changes in that person's body. But this does not account for the healing experienced by those who are absent when "intercessory prayer" is made in their behalf.

The Roman centurion who asked Jesus to simply say the word so that he could know his servant lying sick some miles away would be healed is a case in point. He felt unworthy that Jesus should continue the journey to his house. He felt unworthy for Jesus to enter under his roof. He implored Jesus to simply say

136

the word. He expressed his confidence that just as he himself had authority over his retinue of soldiers, so he knew that if Jesus would simply say the word, his servant would be healed. Jesus was impressed with the centurion's faith. In response to the centurion's request and accompanying faith, Jesus simply spoke the word of assurance and healed his servant immediately. When the centurion's company returned home they found the servant well.[133]

The effectiveness of intercessory prayer has been demonstrated too many times to be set aside as the strokes of chance. Some researchers have attempted to attribute such to a phenomenon they call "mental telepathy". Is this an attempt to leave God out of the human equation?

Jesus made clear that His heavenly Father is ready to answer his followers' prayers. In these instances, it is clear that in response to the prayer of "faith" a *higher power*, outside the individual, is enervating the individual's brain and body producing whatever chemical and physiological changes are needed to bring about healing. This kind of faith looks beyond that which is seen to the One who is unseen, a personal, all-powerful Creator and Healer.

While it is true, as said by Jesus Himself on several occasions of healing, "Thy *faith* hath made thee whole", it is also true that God Himself imbues the mind and body with divine energy to make it whole. The apostle Paul informed the Epicurean and Stoic philosophers of Greece in the city of Athens that "in Him (the Creator of heaven and earth) we live and move and have our being..."[134]

137

William Sadler, after years of successful psychiatric practice, wrote:

"Perfect trust in a Supreme Being is one of the essential steps in the successful treatment and permanent deliverance from the bondage of neuroticism. If our patient's religion does not help him in these matters, if it does not change him, it would be better for him to change his religion and get one that will.

"*Gladstone,* when asked what kept him so serene and composed in the midst of his busy life, replied: "At the foot of my bed, where I can see it on retiring and on arising in the morning, are the words, 'Thou wilt keep him in perfect peace whose mind is stayed on Thee because he trusteth in Thee.'" There is good mental therapeutics in that old method called the "practice of the presence of God."[135]

As the Bible puts it:

" So then faith comes by hearing, and hearing by the word of God." [136]

I have personally found Bible study and the memorization of selected passages to have a profound healing effect on my patients suffering from a wide variety of psychological disorders: anxiety, depression, agoraphobia, panic disorder, obsessive-compulsive disorder, post-traumatic stress disorder, to name a few.

One must be careful in prescribing Bible study as a part of the treatment of neurotics. I had to ask one Bible-reading patient to refrain from Bible study on her own, and to let me join her in Bible study when she came for treatment several times a week to begin with. She was deeply religious, but she had developed a habit of focusing upon the warnings and judgments in Scripture, thus increasing her sense of guilt, her apprehensiveness, her depression, her paranoid thinking, etc. Her method of Bible study made it impossible to get to know God as He really is. She could not see Him as all-wise, all-caring, all-powerful, pure, and holy, because she was failing to read the contexts of the verses she focused on, and failed to get familiar with countless other descriptions of God that would have given her a truly balanced understanding of her loving Creator. She tried to take her life twice before her employer sent her for treatment.

Dr. Sadler especially recommends the Psalms, the Book of Job, the Prophet Isaiah, and the Gospel of John. I have provided my patients with specific passages of Scripture especially appropriate to their special problems such as anxiety, the precursor signals of oncoming depression, their phobias and other problem encounters with people. I have asked these patients to memorize, imagine experiencing, and "over-learn" the verses assigned. Memorization alone is not enough. They must imagine themselves experiencing those verses. See the scene, experience the emotions, sense the touch. And they must over-learn them. They must memorize them so thoroughly that they do not have to search their mind to recall them when needed. I have found that by doing so, whenever the problem situation even begins to threaten them, the appropriate verse will surface in their minds, and the "problem" dissipates. After repeatedly dealing with the problem situation in this manner, the problem ceases to arise at all. The appropriate brain changes have been made.

POSTULATE 14: Love dissipates fear and insecurity

The love referred to here is a principle, not a feeling, although the process of loving is often accompanied by emotion. The principle is outer-directed. As it operates in social relationships it embodies the last six of the Biblical Ten Commandments. As it operates in divine worship it embodies the first four of these Ten Commandments.

This kind of love is said to be the natural outworking of the Holy Spirit in people[137]. In another of his letters, the apostle Paul describes the attitudes and behaviors of all who display the outworking of this principle of love.[138] It is a deep caring for another person.

Love patiently endures suffering for the one loved. Love is kind. Love does not envy. Love does not parade itself. Love is not puffed up. Love does not behave rudely. Love is not selfish. Love is not easily provoked. Love keeps no accounts of evil. Love does not rejoice in iniquity, but rejoices in the truth. Love bears all things, believes all things, hopes all things, and endures all things.

An examination of these consequences of love clearly shows their positive, psychological growth-producing quality. Dr. Borysenko tells the remarkable findings of the epidemiologists as they studied the people of Roseto, Pennsylvania several years ago. Their rate of death from coronary heart disease was very low. The researchers expected to find low levels

142

of the typical major risk factors for coronary disease: cigarette smoking, fat consumption, a sedentary lifestyle, and obesity. Instead, they found that the Rosetans had *terrible* health habits. *They were high in* <u>*all*</u> *the typical risk factors.*

The scientists found that the positive health factor was the social togetherness of the community. There was closeness among the people. They knew one another, their family histories, their joys and sorrows. In Roseto there were plenty of people to listen and to lend a hand when needed.

"Statistics revealed that when people moved *out* of Roseto their rate of heart attack rose to the predicted level. Social support, the great stress buffer, turned out to be more important than health habits in predicting heart disease!" [139]

CHAPTER TWELVE

Self Help That Heals

POSTULATE 15: Healing begins when we walk the walk

Counselors or therapists cannot heal us. They may capture our attention. They may soften our hearts. They may stir our emotions. They may plant words and ideas. They may motivate. They may show the way. They may invite us to follow. They may walk the way with us.

But *we* must walk the walk! We must invest ourselves. *We must energize ourselves into action.* We must *follow through.* We must *endure.* We must *persevere* until the new lifestyle becomes *automatic.* Second nature! A new nature! And the beautiful thing about all of this is that the walk is easy. And we can take it one step at a time!

Psychological growth does not take place without the focused investment of our personal resources. We must become active in working the assignments. These assignments should include appropriate Bible study and prayer. This is vital because they connect us with God, —they help us to develop a relationship with Him, —the true Source of all healing.[140]

Counseling sessions that consist of listening without your personal involvement will not be successful in producing psychological growth.

Furthermore, your perception of the sessions and therapist may deteriorate into negative evaluations, blame, and even rejection of the therapist.

Here are some ways you can help yourself to follow through with your "treatment program":

(1) Take note of your successes, even little ones. Thank God for helping you to follow through with the program. Remember that old habits do not die easily. But don't dwell on them. They weren't formed in a day. Every time you work the program, new nerve growth is taking place. As you pray, those nerves are being charged with a heavenly current direct from the cosmos.[141] And what God begins, He will finish.[142]

(2) Check for any possible difficulties you may have had in doing the assignments. Try to determine why and eliminate the difficulty, or bring it to the attention of the counselor in your next session.

(3) Determine what you really want, as a part of the problem-solving process, before focusing on what you need to do.

(4) Find out how others have "walked the walk".

(5) View videos that vividly portray the healing processes taking place in the brain. As you visualize this healing process you can imagine how your own brain heals. It will facilitate your own healing process.

POSTULATE 16: The mind adapts to whatever it dwells upon.

This principle is well established as a fundamental law of the mind. Numerous controlled studies have demonstrated this. The implications of this principle are extensive. They range from the simplest demonstrations of neural patterns of response to opinion change in the marketplace, politics, and the educational system.

The key to bringing about change is to hold the attention of the person. Obviously, people are turned off by certain mental encounters and fascinated by others. If the obnoxious can be presented in pleasant or innocuous contexts, and has any elements in it that appeal to the senses or the intellect, the mind may return to it again and again. After a time, the obnoxious can actually become pleasurable and in some cases addicting. The mind has adapted because it has had extended exposure to it.

We need to choose the best environment for overcoming a problem. For example, choosing friends that help us overcome and avoiding those that have the same problem. Alcoholics and drug addicts might be examples of the latter. There are times when the environment cannot be changed without violating your conscientious values. In those instances it is best to focus on the good in that environment and to ignore the irritating and the annoying. In His prayer for his disciples, Jesus prayed "I pray not that You should take them out of the world, but that you should keep them from the evil that is in the world."[143]

To a very large extent we may choose, definitely modify, and actually create, our environment. By *mental training* we may develop a new potential—the powerful capacity to choose which course to pursue in the presence of conflicting emotions and an unfavorable environment. We may so train our mind that in the end, our reason, judgment, and choice may become the dominating factor in almost every conflict of life.

In other instances, certain choices of reading, movies, music, etc., may be dwelt upon to the detriment of mental or emotional health.

You may recognize many other situations, both desirable and undesirable for healthy minds, in which the principle governing mind adaptation applies.

POSTULATE 17: Imaging can heal brain nerve patterning

Most of us can imagine a familiar face, house, or room. Often the mental image is experienced as a 'picture in the mind'. Sometimes it is vividly experienced, affecting the emotions and the expectations of the person who is imaging.

Imaging can dramatically change our emotional state. It can arouse new determinations that renounce our self-defeating behaviors and negative self-talk, and promote psychological growth.

We can image particular scenes such as a walk through the woods, or along a riverbank, or by the seashore, —any peaceful, quiet experience. This is one way to induce peaceful, restful feelings when we are anxious or apprehensive.

People who image under these circumstances can recapture the peaceful emotions they have experienced at some time in their life. The associations made unconsciously in their brain of such literal walks with the accompanying feelings of restfulness and peace are reawakened in the imaging experience.

The Psalms and the parables of Jesus provide a rich collection of descriptive life experiences for imaging. Jesus used imagery abundantly in His earthly ministry. An intimate relationship with Jesus generates a host of powerful experiences that become a part of the fabric of our mind. Resurrecting these experiences by imaging will vaporize any threatening cloud. As someone has said, "We have nothing to fear for the future except as we forget the way in which the Lord has led us in the past."

Imaging can help addicts overcome their addictions. People, who are vulnerable to practices of any kind out of weakness when in the presence of certain people, can often find help by visualizing themselves being in the presence of these people and rehearsing their planned way of handling the situation *before* their next encounter.

Connections or associations will be formed in the brain, and when the situation arises the associations will easily form again, and the individual will experience the same strength and decisiveness they experienced in their imaging session.

Re-living your courting days through imaging can help you regenerate the positive experiences of those days. The images awakened during such a session arouse the same romantic emotions you experienced, and current bonding is strengthened.

This does not have to be limited to the days of courting. It may include other pleasant memories of togetherness. Successful unified efforts through times of particular stress in the past can also be relived and visualized.

The formation of mental images of fondest dreams and hopes yet to be fulfilled, adds another dimension to the benefits to be gained from imaging. This exercise awakens hope, assurance, and the will to make the marriage work.

To practice recalling and "re-living" the positive experiences in the past does much to counteract discouragement and depression.

POSTULATE 18: Moderate deprivation typically motivates us.

A moderate level of deprivation sets up a state of need in the person. A sense of need always leads to some kind of activity, some kind of action.

Deprivation----->Need------>Activity

If the actions are appropriate the needs *can* be satisfied. If those actions are pursued long enough without being blocked the needs *will* be satisfied. At this point motivation ceases. It is not activated until a new state of need exists.

Appropriate Actions------>Satisfaction

If the appropriate actions are blocked by outside forces the person feels frustrated.

Appropriate Actions---->||->Frustration

The most common response to frustration is anger. Anger is most often directed toward the perceived source of the "road block" either in the form of rebellion or "acting out". A fight, a temper tantrum, screaming and yelling, tearing up the place are the common expressions of acting out.

Frustration------->Anger---->Acting Out

Anger is sometimes directed inward. Depression then follows often. This is especially true when frustrations have been "the story of the client's life", or at least have been perceived that way.

Inward Directed Anger----->Depression

151

If efforts to satisfy one's needs are inappropriate, restlessness will follow.

Inappropriate Actions----->Restlessness

Later, if the efforts continue to be inappropriate, and if more appropriate options are not found, frustration results and the following sequence will take place.

Frustration----->Sublimation to other satisfactions,

OR ----->Helplessness, Despair

OR----->Escape (fantasy, aimless travel are examples)

OR----->Changing one's values, hence needs.

Needs are here defined not as true needs, but as perceived needs. Hence, it is often the option of the person to modify his perceptions of his needs. This may be a useful alternative for anyone who is at an impasse in his felt frustration.

CHAPTER THIRTEEN

Establishing Patterns That Last

POSTULATE 19: Strong lifestyle patterns are formed during the first three years and again during puberty.

During the first three years after birth, our brain is extremely active. As new brain cells and networks emerge learning is phenomenal. Our learning in turn stimulates the growth of more new networks. The newly developing brain delivers its generous supply of hormones. As a result, the body's entire immune system is formed and programmed, and emotional response patterns and lifestyle patterns are 'blue-printed'.

'Imprinting', vividly demonstrated in animal experiments, takes place during the earliest period of maturation and development. For example, chicks have rejected their mother hen, choosing to follow a wooden duckling instead. From the time they were hatched they were deprived of their mother, and exposed to a mechanically moving wooden duck. They became attached to the wooden duck!

Among humans, the first two or three years of life are critical for emotional, mental, and social bonding to take place. When both parents, father **and** mother, form healthy loving and caring attachments to their infants (both male and female) during this time, their infants easily develop healthy caring social relationships. These healthy parental attachments will imprint the infants with heterosexual capacities for loving and caring throughout their lifetime.

I do not think it accidental for example, that I have never treated a male homosexual who has had a positive, bonding relationship with his father during this imprinting period. Sexual orientation is imprinted by secretion of hormones at this time.[144] Sadly, many well-meaning parents have been ignorant of these facts, and difficulties in their own life adjustments at the times critical for bonding with their children robbed them of the joys of that early bonding with their children. Many factors can contribute to this failure in parental bonding. We who have avoided such failure need to exemplify our loving Savior, who reminded us that,

"God did not send His Son into the world to condemn the world, but that the world through Him might be saved."[145]

In addition, when brain centers responsible for the positive emotions such as love, trust, joy, etc. are activated, hormones increase their flow, and the development of the immune system operates in high gear!

Again during puberty hormone activity reaches another extremely high peak. During this time emotions are strongly experienced, and there is a new spurt in the sprouting of brain networks. Lifestyle patterns laid down during the first three years can be greatly strengthened. during puberty. Healthy heterosexual love relationships and social skills can receive a new boost in strength. Healthy bonding can be easily strengthened.

During this period of puberty, a new window of opportunity opens for shaping new learning, for strengthening the body's immune system, and for correcting lifestyle patterns. Imperfect patterns laid down during the first three years of infancy can be modified at this time, though in some cases with difficulty. I have found in a few instances that even healthy heterosexual bonding, if lacking, can be formed during puberty.

In addition, research has shown that deep-seated long lasting attachments to our loving Creator can be and are made during puberty.

Research has shown that when emotion immediately follows learning or performance, the learning and ability to perform are long lasting. How critically important it is that our learning during puberty be of the highest quality.

The plasticity of the brain and the rapid multiplication of communication and experiential networks in the brain are phenomenal during these two early periods of development. The immune system, critical to a healthy lifetime, is laid down during these times and renews itself at a mind-boggling rate. During the time it takes you to read this short sentence, that immune system can produce ten million new lymphocytes and a million billion new antibody molecules!

Beyond this, *templates* are laid down to provide the patterns for development throughout the rest of the individual's life! Sexual orientations are formed.

Positive or negative mental attitudes are programmed. Healthy or perverted appetites (hungers) are begun. Pugnacity (the drive to hurt or destroy) or the Peacemakers Drive is patterned.

Our young people need to be impressed with these life-shaping facts. What wonderful opportunities they have to shape happy, healthy, and truly fulfilling lives. During their puberty years, many delinquent young people have changed the direction of their lives, and become positive and highly successful leaders, molding the thoughts and lives of others. The years of puberty open new windows of opportunity for healing, for growth and change

POSTULATE 20: Self-denial fortifies against stress

All of us have had occasions when we have needed to deny ourselves of some indulgence -- to lose weight, protect our heart, attend to some responsibility, nourish our minds with worthwhile subjects. As unpleasant as these acts of self-denial may be, they actually help us to cope with stress later on.

I had a college roommate once who ate shredded wheat (or was it Ruskets?)[146] with water and nothing else for breakfast. We had developed a close friendship, and I invited him to have breakfast on me in the cafeteria one morning thinking he was short of cash. He replied,

"No, I have money, but I feel like I might have to do without someday, and I want to be prepared."

He was released from prison in China recently after many long years spent in confinement with little to eat! After his release I corresponded with him, and saw pictures of him taken shortly after. I read several of his scholarly articles written a short time after his release. Months later, when he was permitted to visit America, he attended our college graduating class reunion, and I had the treasured privilege of embracing him and visiting with him. My wife and I, and large numbers of our classmates were amazed and so very grateful that he came through that prison ordeal self-disciplined and healthy in body and mind! He would tell you that it was the Lord that sustained him, and take no credit for his ability to withstand the privations he experienced.

Brain and body can better equip us for stress that is beyond our control when we practice a little self-denial each day. Such self-denial need not and should not be extreme. Neither should it be like the man who said he was denying himself of watermelon during Lent when there were no watermelons!

But you might follow self-denial with some small reward the first few times. You won't have to continue these rewards later. After a little while the sense of self-mastery will be rewarding enough.

POSTULATE 21: Mind events that occur together tend to reoccur together

Have you ever gone to the other end of the house to do something, and when you got there you forgot what you went for? We all have. And feeling stupid, perhaps, we went back to where we came from and the moment we arrived, we remembered!

The elements in the original setting had become associated with the thoughts that caused us to travel to the other side of the house! The characteristics of the elements in the room had become associated with our plans and assisted us in the recall.

One study found that students taking a final examination in the same room in which the class lectures were given, earned higher scores than similar students who had to take the final examination in a room different from the one in which they received the lectures.

Once I had to take an examination out of the regular schedule. The professor allowed me to write the exam in his office. Of course, I had never done any of my studying in his office. After awhile he returned and asked, "How are you coming?" I answered, "Fine, except for three questions. I know the answers but I just can't recall them just now. I asked the professor if I might just step across the hall into the room where I had studied that material. He knew that the answers weren't in that room, and so he said "sure, go right ahead." The moment I entered that room, the answers came to my mind! When I returned to the professor's office, and told him I recalled the answers, he commented, "Isn't it wonderful, how the mind works!" He knew the law of mental associations.

CHAPTER FOURTEEN

Family Dynamics that Heal

POSTULATE 22: Reward is more effective than punishment in changing behavior

Someone has said that parents would be more successful in child-rearing if they would more often "catch 'em being good" and reward them with a smile of approval, a pat on the back, a word of gratitude and appreciation.

Rewarding should be frequent and intermittent. The behavior that has been reinforced in this way will last. A child is likely to repeat the positive behavior even when it isn't noticed, if his behavior has met with approval from time to time.

Punishment is necessary some of the time. Nevertheless, punishment has been shown to be least effective in *correcting* behavior. This is especially the case when the person has difficulty replacing the unwanted behavior with something positive.

Furthermore, when an authority figure (a parent, for example) inflicts forced physical punishment, he unwittingly communicates the message that "might makes right." The child learns to physically "punish" others that are weaker.

If the authority figure loses control in the punishing process, he not only is guilty of physical abuse, but also is providing a model for violence.

POSTULATE 23: Modeling is one of the most powerful methods of teaching.

We learn best by seeing it done -- by seeing it enacted. Supervisors of on-the-job trainees agree. This principle is most important for children during their impressionable years. This fact needs to be ingrained in parents trying to manage their families.

Frequently when dealing with child behavior problems, I have seen children's behavior change when parents corrected their style of management, and their modeling behavior.

POSTULATE 24: Counterbalancing in family tends toward stabilizing the family.

The father was frustrated because of his wife's leniency with the children, and the wife was frustrated because of the husband's strictness. Another father was panicking over the prospect of financial disaster because his wife was "throwing hard-earned money to the wind", and the wife was bitter over her husband who "was stingy, selfish, and tightfisted" with money. "What is money for if it is not to spend!" she screamed. A son begs his sister not to embarrass him with her "worldly dress style" and the sister expresses her astonishment that her brother is so suddenly concerned about what others think.

These polarized positions are typical as families attempt to bring homeostasis to the family unit. Homeostatic adjustments are natural attempts of the family unit to preserve itself. If the unit moves outside a range of comfortable existence, at least one member will try to pull it back. But the process is stressful to the family unit.

It is easy for you to see me as extreme, and for me to see you as being extreme in the opposite direction. Our efforts to correct each other are from the best of motives. We want moderation, not extremism.

POSTULATE 25: Interrupting the newborn's brain development results in its malformation.

Alcohol. Even mild alcohol use by mothers before they know they are pregnant, can result in widespread brain damage. The damage has been found to include attention disorders, behavioral disabilities, hyperactivity, temper tantrums, impulsiveness, short memory span, and perceptual disorders that interfere with learning.

Heavier alcohol use by pregnant mothers can result in mental retardation, improperly formed limbs and heart, stunted physical growth, and physical facial deformities. The brains of these developing infants frequently remain small, shrunken, and improperly formed.

Although the first reported controlled scientific study on the offspring of drinking and non-drinking mothers was conducted by William Sullivan, a Liverpool physician, in the year 1899, warnings to mothers-to-be about alcohol can be traced back to Old Testament biblical times.

In Judges 13:7, an angel tells the wife of Manoah, "Behold, you shall conceive and bear a son; and now drink no wine or strong drink."

The warning was heeded, and a healthy child named Samson was born.

It was not until 1973 that the frightening pattern of gruesome development resulting from alcohol use by expectant mothers was described by Dr. Sterling K. Clarren and his colleagues at the Pediatric

Department of the University of Washington School of Medicine in Seattle. He called this frightening pattern "fetal alcohol syndrome".[147] If subtle behavioral problems can arise from even small amounts of alcohol taken by expectant mothers, women need to be informed of these serious risks. Often expectant mothers consume large amounts of alcohol in prescription and over-the-counter medicines such as cough syrup in a heavy alcohol base.

The case history intake of children suffering from any of the above abnormalities should include information on the mother's possible use of alcohol at any time in the past and the likelihood of alcohol use during her pregnancy.

Ionic Radiation. Two months into pregnancy, Nurumi, Toda's mother stood half a mile from where the atomic bomb was dropped on Hiroshima. Consequently Nurumi suffers from mental retardation.[148]

Alcohol causes the nerve cells to migrate past their destinations in their developmental growth. Radiation causes these nerve cells to stop short of reaching their destinations. Brain cells have to develop properly to do the right thing. These are the observations coming from at least forty years of research on Hiroshima survivors.

The nuclear reactor meltdown at Chernobyl on April 26, 1986 has resulted in scientists predicting that mental retardation from that disaster will be five times that which normally occurs in the general population.

Tobacco, and malnutrition should be added to the list of causes for fetal malformation, prematurity, and gross learning disabilities.

It is clear that what the mother eats, drinks, and breathes can have a profound influence on the development of the infant's mind.

Even the mother's crowded living conditions, and her stressed emotional state during the fetal development in her womb will take its toll in the developing mind of the child.

POSTULATE 26: New learning multiplies brain cell networks

Brain cell fibers actually grow toward appropriate cell destinations to make synaptic connections with those cells in response to our efforts to learn. Repeated efforts produce continuing growth until the synapse (connection) is made. This process is considerably easier during the first year of a child's life, because there are lots of brain cells that are not yet hooked up in response to the learning and performing that such connections make possible. Likewise, as the number of synapses increases, the learning and responding increases.

Studies during the past twenty-five years have shown that even during adulthood, new brain cell hookups are made as we pay attention to learning and performing specific tasks. As more and more of the brain is committed to their functions, it becomes more difficult for newly growing brain cell fibers to find territory in which to synapse.

It is my guess that most of us could continue to learn if we were willing to persevere in our efforts. I suspect that too many people give up their efforts with many cell fibers partly grown toward fulfilling their objective, but abandoned just short of making the needed connections.

Even older people who remain active in work are likely to find a continuing purpose in life, are less inclined to functional depression, and are more often motivated to depend upon themselves and their own resources. If their environment includes vigorous involvement with family and friends, an active rather than passive life-style, and flexible attitudes, they are more likely to retain mental sharpness. Being active in a wider variety of pursuits tends to preserve mental sharpness in a wider range of mental abilities. Older people who live with their families or maintain an active social life out-performed others who lived alone.

Professor Schaie believes that mental exercises, like physical exercises, can help older people sustain and in some instances even improve their mental capabilities. "It's very much like physical skills: once you stop using them, they get rusty."[149]

Unfortunately, there are diseases that overtake the brain that interfere with its plasticity and development. Most of these occur in the later years of life. Scientists are busy at work trying to solve these problems that interfere with the growth and development of the human mind.

One therapist demonstrated that perseverance pays off. His patient had suffered a leg injury. His ankle had been partly crushed. After appropriate orthopedic surgery, his foot remained in a cast over a period of nearly two years. When the cast was removed, he was still unable to move his foot on demand.

Using biofeedback technology, the therapist demonstrated to the patient that the nerves required for the movement of his foot were still alive. When he put forth efforts to move his foot, the patient saw the biofeedback instrument report nerve activity even though he couldn't move his foot. His effort to move

170

his foot activitated the nerve networks to repair and grow.

By repeating these efforts several times a day, in less than two weeks the patient was able to move his foot on demand. Apparently the peripheral nerve endings had been damaged in the injury. They needed to regenerate, grow and make their connections with the appropriate muscles. They did just that in response to being stimulated by the "efforts" put forth to move that foot.

Clients who "give up too soon" need to understand that their brain cells are responding to their efforts, whether they see any evidence of it or not. This has its application in the learning of virtually any mental task, given that the brain development has not been irreversibly interfered with. With more brain cells than any of us could possibly use in our lifetime, there are untold numbers of new connections waiting to be made. And remember that current neuroscience has established that new brain cells are being formed all the time, especially in response to new efforts!

POSTULATE 27: Redundancy and plasticity may offset brain cell loss during aging.

Beginning shortly after birth when the maximum number of brain cells that we will probably possess are in place, brain cells begin to die at a frightening rate according to Dr. Stanley Rapaport of the National Institute on aging. The maximum the rate is thought to be about fifty thousand per day. Multiply that by the number of days you have lived and you could get some staggering figures.[150] That's about eighteen and one-quarter million cells every year!

In spite of this, brain performance in healthy people does not significantly change over a fifty- year period, and for some people, performance actually improves even into the mid-seventies and older.

The principle of *redundancy* simply says that we have so many more brain cells than we could possibly use, and so we can afford to lose a tremendous number. The principle "use it or lose it" may be directing this massive extermination of brain cells. Is it possible that we are not providing our brain with the enrichment of fascinating opportunities that our brain is capable of handling?

In spite of the death of millions of brain cells, undamaged brain cells in the elderly can grow more dendrites, providing more communication sites. That is the principle of *plasticity*. Those fewer brain cells are more active and search out new connections if they are called upon to perform, even in advancing years. The more experience the greater the number of connections. More learning forms more brain connections. More practice produces more brain connections.

Decreases in memory span and in the ability to process information rapidly, and to integrate incoming information become frightening or discouraging to many who are aging. Encouraging them by informing them that the most recent studies are showing that even the physical loss or deterioration of thousands of brain cells per day does not necessarily reduce the functioning potential of an aging person. It will take a little longer to process some tasks, perhaps, but the lack of speed can be more than offset by the *wisdom of their experience* definitely lacking among the young. And it is very possible that most of these "losses" in function can be halted or even reversed by practice. The bottom line is that the plasticity of the brain can continue even in the oldest years.

POSTULATE 28: Habituation weakens the consequences.

Parents are often exasperated over their inability to motivate their children. They try reward or punishment to no avail. The problem may be *habituation*.

Think of punishment as a stimulus intended to bring discomfort, pain, or loss. If the same stimulus is repeatedly applied, the stimulus soon loses its "punishing" quality. The nervous system, not only the pain sensors but mind processes as well, habituate to the "familiar" stimulus.

What was once rewarding quickly loses its rewarding quality if repeatedly applied. Boredom sets in, because the nervous system habituates to repeated stimuli.

Many parents try to make their punishment take effect by punishing "harder" and "harder". But habituation to the lower level of pain tends to reduce the aversive effect of the next higher level of punishing.

This principle of habituation operates because of the adaptive nature of the nervous system. Habituation operates across virtually every experience we could have. Repeating the same experience over and over again eventually neutralizes its impact on our response systems.

POSTULATE 29: Habituation predicts boredom.

People become bored when they encounter the same experience over and over again. Brilliant children tire of doing assignments that do not teach them new concepts. Facts are important only as they can be integrated into new frameworks.

Scientists used to believe that infants and very small children have severely restricted ability to abstract. Current research is proving otherwise. Children are more interested in seeing relationships, and in integrating discrete bits of information into complex structures, than they are just accumulating facts.

Watch an infant as he attends to a dangling toy above his crib. As quickly as the infant has grasped the information available about that dangling toy, he will attend to something else.

Often what is thought to be a "short attention span" is boredom because the concepts are quickly grasped. We can provide these children with more variety, more challenging tasks, and more novelty.

We all need some repetition of sameness for habits to be established in the reverberating circuits of the brain, but the established habit must better equip the client for totally novel experiences as soon as the habit is formed. This is our only assurance we will be motivated for change.

Even in the drug culture we see the powerful principle of habituation at work. In spite of the pleasurable "high" received from a particular drug, one

177

drug user remarked as he prepared to inject himself again, "What am I doing this for?" Boredom was setting in. Typically these go to adding other drugs for novel additions to their drug adventures--to overcome the habituation that has begun to set in.

Our brain is built for exploring new worlds. It wants to create new brain cells, to replace dying brain cells, to make new connections, to learn new things about us and the universe. So if you find yourself getting bored with life, see if you've gotten into some ruts that keep you from exploring. Try making simple changes. Doing little things a little differently—trying a different recipe, wearing a different combination, getting acquainted with a different person, reading a different kind of book, traveling to a different place. In all of this exploring, you don't need to discard your deep-seated values. Carry them with you as you explore your new worlds. There are billions out there.

POSTULATE 30: Experience shapes our concepts

Our interpretations of events in our homes, our community, our world are filtered through our past experience. Genetic programming undoubtedly plays a part. Perhaps more often as pre-dispositions or tendencies rather than absolute push-button programming.

Our experiences are so varied. No two people have had identical experiences. Hence, the challenge of understanding one another and communicating with one another is ever with us. Modern technology and massive communication media reduce the differences in the experiences of people around the world. But challenging differences remain.

One of the major tasks with interpersonal relationships including marriage and family relationships, is to "see things through the other person's eyes"—to "sit where others sit", and feel how others feel.

I have found that by modeling good listening and empathic responding as I interact with people, I am more successful in teaching them this essential skill. It is vital if people are going to get along with each other.

Having a few practice sessions with them helps them to learn by doing. If the family is in the session together, a practice session with each other is helpful.

In the listening process am I really hearing the other person. Am I seeing and experiencing the particular situations as *they* perceive it and experience it.

One test as to whether or not I am really in tune with the other person is that I am totally non-judgmental or even evaluative about what I am hearing. Certainly the other person is not being judgmental about their perceptions. Neither should we be. And we will not, if we are really attuned to what they are experiencing.

I know that I must listen very intently to truly catch the spirit and the essence of what our friends or family members are trying to say. By doing this I expand my background of experience and modify and broaden my understanding of their worlds. Every new encounter, if attended to, and experienced for what it really is, can add new exciting dimensions to our world of understanding.

POSTULATE 31: Caring probing promotes peace and understanding.

Caring probing encourages others to open up with a sense of freedom to tell their story. It relaxes them. It motivates them. It helps them to zero in on their real concerns. Let's see how we can use it in family communication.

Carkhuff[151] emphasizes that probing should never be a question and answer session. I would add, never should probing be a cross- examination—an important rule in family communication.

Caring probing is usually open-ended, —a statement or question that does not expect a 'yes' or 'no' answer. It is a statement or question that communicates genuine respect for the one to whom it is addressed. It communicates the attitude of a genuine and interested learner. It does not come from one who "thinks he knows the answer". Caring probing opens the way for understanding the issue or situation as the other person understands it—for seeing it as he sees it. If you see it just as the other person sees it, if you were "walking in his shoes", if you were "sitting where he sits", you would never be inclined to condemn or fault that person. Every way of a person is right in his own eyes.[152] His way of dealing with a situation may not have been right. But only God can understand the way his brain worked to shape the way he sees the situation.

Sometimes you will lose the other person's train of thought: "I'm sorry, I am not sure I was following you just then." Sometimes you may need to help them shift the focus to get the fuller picture: "I notice that everything you have said about Susie is negative. Maybe that is *all there is* to say about her?"

Caring probes lead us to fruitful self-discovery. They help us gain new perspectives, new courage, and new coping skills. They never put others on the defensive. No one is ever on the witness stand.

Such probing helps us avoid the habit of giving advice. It gets away from telling others what to do. Instead, it leads others to discover their options, to weigh them, and to make their own choices.

Caring probing is about learning to love other people, even those that may have annoyed or irritated you. As you listen to *their* story your understanding and your caring about them grows. After it's all over, you'll feel good inside for not pre-judging them and for really caring.

POSTULATE 32: The mind has a powerful influence on the body.

Bible writers were well informed on what scientists are beginning to demonstrate about the profound influence of the mind on the body.

About a thousand years before the time of Jesus, the wise man King Solomon, wrote:

"A merry (joyful, happy) heart (mind, inner being) does good like a medicine,

But a broken spirit dries the bones."[153]

(An alternate translation reads "makes medicine even better").

Frustrated over the widely different and often unpredictable outcomes of medication and surgery with different people, new approaches have been sought in recent years. Enriched and strengthened by the rigorous and carefully controlled work of experimental psychologists, medical men have noted the psychological connections between a wide variety of diseases, mental attitudes and focused thinking.

The literature describes prescriptions of different mental exercises to treat virtually every category of diseases including ulcers, gall bladder, colitis, heart condition, obesity, diabetes, cancer, *ad infinitum.*

Benson and his colleages have identified several body responses to simple relaxation exercises.[154] Blood pressures have been lowered, blood flow has been increased, rapid heart rates have been slowed, and mental alertness has been improved. The

183

simple trick of taking a deep breath and imagining you in your favorite nature spot, perhaps by a quiet stream, can greatly help the entire body system to relax. Follow this by thinking "my, this feels good!" and you may mobilize an entire army in your immune system.

Psychologists Jean Achterberg and G. Frank Lawlis[155] have demonstrated the power of imaging, (visualizing in one's mind). They have seen their patients visualize their white cells like soldiers surrounding their cancer cells and destroying them. As a consequence the patient's immune system performed the astounding recruitment of white cells and destroyed the cancer cells. Tests revealed that in each case the white cell count rose dramatically in response to such positive thinking, and in each case the spread of cancer cells was arrested.

These researchers have developed a model to describe the mechanisms for the interaction between mind and body. I will let them describe the background and nature of their model:

"The model is derived principally from the work of Hans Selye[156] and involves much of what is known about the physiological concomitants of stress. The emotions accompanying stress--fear, anxiety, and depression--are reflected in limbic system activity, which directly involves hypothalamic and pituitary function. The pituitary, the body's master gland, regulates all hormonal activity. Furthermore, imbalances in hormonal activity have frequently been demonstrated to be connected to increases in malignant growth. Oversecretion of the adrenal has been particularly noted to affect the thymus and lymph integrity and subsequently the white blood cells. Stress can thus be viewed as having a twofold influence on the malignant process: (1) the production of abnormal cells increases, and (2) the capability of the body to destroy these cells is diminished. Imagery moving in a positive direction may serve to alleviate the disruptive emotional condition and thereby intervene in the stress-disease-stress cycle." [157]

So take hold of your mind. Decide that you are turning over every care to your loving Great Physician[158], and tell yourself you are so glad you did! The peace that will come over you will feel wonderful. You will be actively participating in the healing of the brain.

CHAPTER FIFTEEN

Planning Ahead

POSTULATE 33: Only Positive Thinkers Are Winners.

Jim had gone through one divorce, and now he was contemplating another. His first wife divorced him. His present wife ordered him out of the house. It was her house when he married her. He lost his job because of company cutbacks. He is skilled in his trade, conscientious, but plagued with guilt-feelings. He gets a new job in another part of the country. One part of his new job would be better handled if he had more training. He sends off for a correspondence course, completes it, and upgrades himself with the new skill attested to by a Certificate of Mastery.

When he thinks about his failed marriages, his job performance suffers, he loses his appetite, and spirals into depression. He even wishes he did not have to go on with life.

When he thinks about his job accomplishments, the expressed appreciation of his boss, the letter of high recommendation from the previous job from which he was terminated, he is buoyant and clear thinking.

When he thinks about his children's warmth toward him, children of the first marriage he smiles and speaks fondly of them even though they are battling with problems of their own. During the times of these positive thoughts and reflections, he takes charge of his life, and executes his responsibilities with enviable skill and devotion.

In 1983 Daly and Burton reviewed the literature on irrational beliefs and found them correlated with a host of psychological problems: depression, social anxiety, coronary-prone behavior, and lack of assertion.

Our thinking clearly directs our coping styles. Whenever I have slipped into negative thinking, I have actually created many more problems for myself. Negative thinking is a formula for losers.

So as soon as you catch your mind headed for unpleasant territory—worry, anxiety, blame, fault-finding, resentment, bitterness, etc.—smile at yourself. Turn around and ask yourself if you have to feel that way. You might get a drink of cool, refreshing water, go out for a breath of fresh air, start thinking of somebody you can thank, or do something good for somebody. It's amazing how interrupting your negative thinking with little positive thoughts can begin instant healing.

POSTULATE 34: The Ability to Focus is Essential for Self-Control.
The secret to controlling your behavior is to pay attention to what you are doing. In your earlier years your feelings triggered your actions. You did a lot of things on impulse without thinking, or with just a flashing thought. As you passed through childhood and adolescence into adulthood, more of your behavior became thoughtful and purposeful.

In my private practice, I have seen many whose impulsivity scores are very high. These people have difficulty paying attention to what they are doing. They make more careless mistakes when they are measuring the ingredients for a cake or balancing a checkbook. They are more frequently in accidents, regretful over hasty decisions they have made, and embarrassed over their rash expenditures. One client scoring a ten (the highest possible) on the impulsivity scale on the Sixteen Personality Factor Test was chided by her husband for giving the waitress a ten dollar tip for a twelve dollar meal!

Attention-deficit disorders are on the rise in our society. The fallout from this disorder includes poor grades in school, increased number of accidents, irresponsibility and undependability, and many others.

If we pay attention to what we are doing, we can better control our behavior.

Here are a few suggestions to build control into your focus:

- Sleep on so-called bargains before purchasing.
- Restrict purchases to absolute necessities for six weeks or longer.
- Put the first 10% or more of your earnings into the ministry of your church.
- Practice being careful in each thing you do.
- Practice being accepting of criticism.
- Strive to be conscientious in what you do.
- Practice being on guard in your behavior.
- Practice smiling when you need to be patient.
- Practice saying something kind when about to lose your temper.

If you practice a number of the above suggestions for six weeks or longer, you will have laid down reinforced pathways in your brain, and focused attention will become natural for you. Always begin with the easiest until you have mastered it. Then proceed with the next easiest and so on through the list.

POSTULATE 35: The Law of Entropy calls for a back-up plan

Any long-term plan you set out to perform tends to fall apart. Your New Year's resolutions are examples. There are many others you can think of. What's worse, you know your plans were good plans. They would really help to put your life in order and make you successful and happy. Then why do they fall apart? How can we keep that from happening?

Many scientists believe that the general trend of the universe is toward death and disorder. They believe the universe is simply following the Law of Entropy. Philosophers suggest that our *plans* are simply following that same Law!

Unless we can overcome that Law and interrupt that trend, we will develop a pessimistic outlook on life. We will become skeptics about everything. We will get discouraged, and sometimes totally depressed. Unless we can interrupt that trend we will become quite fatalistic!

On the other hand, *thermodynamics*, a branch of physics dealing with the mechanics and relations of heat, hints a ray of hope. Let me illustrate.

Heat can provide energy, and energy can accomplish work. For a physicist *entropy is the amount of energy in a system that is **not** available for doing work.* Obviously if you don't have energy for work, work isn't going to get done.

But the physicist is optimistic. He knows that he can get more work done if he can get more energy out of the heat. And he's figured out that he could get more energy out of the heat *by simply changing its temperature!* In other words, by a simple change in temperature he has changed the amount of energy available to get the work done.

So it is for us. Often, just a simple change in one thing affecting our plan will keep it from falling apart. So, to keep your plan from falling apart, look for some simple thing to keep it going.

Maybe a back-up plan, a little diversity (like walking a different route), getting somebody to join you, choosing somebody to report to, breaking it down into a few smaller plans, setting check-up times to see how your plan is coming, etc. You may feel like a million dollars! You'll feel like you can conquer the world. And, of course, this up-beat spirit is healing for both brain and body.

POSTULATE 36: A Force Field analysis can increase the probability of healing

You need to consider the positive and negative forces that will impact on your plan for healing. Forces that will propel you along toward your goal are positive forces. Those that will hinder you from achieving your objective are negative forces. Both kinds of forces are at work all the time.

Some of these forces, positive or negative, are manageable. You can decide how much influence they will have on your journey toward healing. On the other hand, some of these forces you will be wiser to simply avoid. You will be unable to do anything with them.

You need to analyze the field forces that are already at work in your life and those that will be operating in any plan that you follow to achieve healing. Some of these forces are in your environment, both physical and social, and even spiritual, i.e., in the unseen cosmos.

Some of them lie inside of you. They are a part of your make-up, biological and psychological. If you analyze these field forces, both within and without, you will be better prepared to relate to them. You may not know *why* they work as they do, but your analysis will help you to take advantage of the way in which they work.

Be honest with yourself. As you plan to put your planned healing strategies into operation, ask yourself if the time slots you have set aside are realistic. Has this kind of time-slotting worked for you before? If not, why not? Why should it work now? What do you have going for you now that you didn't when such planning didn't work? What real specific benefits can you imagine from your planned healing strategies? Are these the kind of benefits others have gained from a similar plan? Will the benefits be worth the effort? What possible obstacles to reaching your goals might you expect? Can you see yourself overcoming those obstacles? How will you overcome the worst of them?

This process of analyzing the positive and negative forces that will bear upon you and your journey toward healing, will allow you to build on your strengths and avoid the pitfalls in that journey. You will be more certain of making the trip successfully.

POSTULATE 37: The Principle of Inertia predicts that we resist changing our lifestyle.

In a professional seminar on personality trait structure, a contemporary psychologist remarked:

"I have been in the business of trying to help people change for nearly thirty years, and I am a discouraged man. People simply do not change."

Most of us tend to get into ruts of behavioral patterns. We repeat the same patterns of thinking, emotional responding, and doing. We may make minor adjustments, but the overall direction of our life is the same. Even when these lifestyle patterns are self-defeating, we continue to repeat them.

When we discover that we aren't happy with the way life is going for us, we may think about seeking professional help. But we seldom anticipate making any significant lifestyle changes. Even if we do feel that we need to make some significant changes, like quitting smoking, or losing weight, or getting rid of our obsessions or compulsions, reducing our stress load, quitting our job, etc., making major changes doesn't come easy.

So how do we make changes that are not easy to make? The secret is to break those changes down into easy steps. Make a habit of practicing some easy strategies that will prepare you for the harder ones. Gradually move on to more difficult strategies until you are finally able to handle the most difficult ones with ease.

In my development of an action program for my clients, I explore with them a variety of self-help strategies or exercises that others have found helpful under similar circumstances. But since people are different, strategies that are easy for some people are more difficult for others.

We select the strategies that the client and I agree upon, and assign the easiest three or four to begin with. The idea is that after they have practiced those that are easiest for them, and are successful in those exercises, they will be better prepared in both attitude and ability to do the next exercises that were not quite as easy. They are usually ready for a new set of exercises each week or two.

It is not important that you make drastic changes in your program overnight. What is important is that you do something in the direction of change for the better. You will then be moving off "dead center". The rest of the journey will be easier. It's getting started that's tough.

POSTULATE 38: You *can* control whatever controls you.
We are all familiar with Jesus' instruction that we pray "Lead us not into temptation". Such a prayer acknowledges the likelihood that whatever tempts us may control us.

B. F. Skinner went farther than that. He insisted that our environment controls all of us. He demonstrated over and over again that, by changing the environment, he could change the behavior. He stirred up a lot of argument and anger over that claim. People don't like to be manipulated. When people insisted that you can lead a horse to water, but you can't make him drink, Skinner's reply was, "Oh, yes, you can. Give him salt!" Skinner's message was "If you change the environment, you will change the behavior".

While I agree that we are too easily manipulated by our environment, we have shown in our earlier chapters that we *can* control what we attend to, and we can make choices that over-ride outside influences to shape our behavior. (Chapters 3 and 4)

Self-defeating behaviors are *typically* triggered by the reoccurrence of specific cues that trigger the behavior. Our responses in that environment tend to become associated or connected with the environment. Our responses then become part of the network of brain connections with that environment. That is one reason we respond in the same way without thinking the next time that we're in the same situation

197

This phenomenon of brain network formation helps us to recall past memories, to relive past experiences in our imagination, and to remember how we solved a particular problem.

For those who have not yet strengthened their will and their power to choose wisely, if they want to eliminate the practice of over-eating, the fridge or kitchen counter must not be stocked with the tempting snacks. We cannot eliminate the food "stimulus" completely. We must eat to survive. But we can limit the amount of ready-made foods available to us.

Another strategy would be to severely restrict the amount of food we prepare for each meal. Still another would be to eliminate the availability of high calorie foods in our fridge, pantry or on the counter. The apostle Paul put it simply when he said, "make no provision for the flesh, to fulfill the lusts thereof." (Romans 13:14) By doing any of these simple things, we would control the things in our environment that control us.

There's another little trick that works wonders. We can change the way we see that controlling trickster! We see it as tricky, deceptive, and self-destructive: It is "sweet to the taste" but bitter in my body and brain, ruining my health, my ability to think clearly and to really be in charge over the long haul. It wants to give my immune system a hard time, to clog up my blood vessels and give me a stroke or heart attack. It wants to kill me! And when we see it all that way, we will never want to let it control us. We will be in control of what controls us.

POSTULATE 39: Painful buried memories can be displaced by the grace of our Divine Creator.
Many clients come for therapy because they cannot find relief from a tormenting memory. The memory of abusing a child or other loved one or being abused, of murder committed, of cheating, of gross and deliberate lying. These are tormenting memories!

Often the memories cannot be confessed to those that have been wronged. They have died, are nowhere to be found, or have lost their capacity for comprehension. The load of guilt becomes unbearable. Many have committed suicide because they could find no relief.

Some have gone to professionals for relief, and have gotten worse. They were misled with well-intended, nevertheless subtly *flawed* techniques and suppositions. Fortunately, for others, they have come to counselors that have truly helped them to experience healing and relief. But many cannot afford professional counseling.

Much of the suffering during the period of bereavement is from tormenting memories. Sometimes the memories are distorted or magnified in a highly sensitized mind. They are painful, nevertheless. And they continue to haunt. They recur like an obsession.

In dealing with the pain do not try to minimize the memory. Do not act as if the memory is not something you should be pained about. Accept the pain, but turn it all over to the Divine Counselor. He asks you to give Him your burden.[159] He asks you to

199

cast **your entire** burden upon Him.[160]He is touched with your painful memories. He knows your desperation for relief. He **treats you with sacred regard because He created you, and then bought you back with His lifeblood shed on Calvary while we were yet sinners.**

We may feel the need of a personal human counselor. We may feel that we don't know how to go to the Divine Counselor. If this is the case, go to a competent Christian counselor. As you seek professional help, remember that there are some risks involved. The following principles can help you to avoid the risks. Remember,

- The counselor should **never encourage the disclosure of** any trespass, personal violation of conscience, specific sin or wrong committed against anyone other than the counselor.

- The counselor should never encourage the client to resurrect memories of the prior abuses they may have experienced.

Typically, many counselors today do just the opposite. But in my opinion, these are needlessly taking great risks and are deceived by *apparent* results. Let me explain:

Guilt feelings can be devastatingly tormenting. I can eliminate those guilt feelings by private confession and repentance to my God in whom I believe. Or I can effectively reduce and sometimes eliminate those guilt feelings by private confession to my counselor or another confidant in whom I believe.

I experience either freedom from or significant reduction in my feelings of guilt when I believe I am still accepted as a person of worth after my disclosure. Everyone experiences emotional catharsis or relief when they simply unload their feelings. Of course, sometimes that unloading can lead to further emotional concerns. But in general, people do find relief after 'unloading' their grief to a sympathetic ear. So where is the problem with confession to the sympathetic *human* ear?

The problem lies with our humanity—the humanity of the confessor and the humanity of the hearer(s). The very rehearsal of sin lessens and eventually wipes out our sense of its "awfulness". More than a few "hearers" of these confessions have fallen into the same sins, both laymen and professionals—even preachers and priests! More than a few grief-stricken confessing persons have fallen again and often into worse sins than before. Why? Because the confession has reduced the sense of its awfulness.

Why is there a difference when we confess these crippling experiences to our Highest Power? Because He relieves us of the burden of our guilt-feelings by directly wiping out those burdensome brain connections. He replaces them with newly created brain cell connections, new impulses, new tendencies, pure passions, new memories of past victories, and new energies to "go, and sin no more".

How do I know this? Because of the changed lives of thousands I know personally that have confirmed specific Bible promises. For instance this one:

"Therefore if anyone is in Christ, he is a **new creation**; old things have passed away; behold, **all** things have become new."[161] And this one: "be transformed by the **renewing** of your mind"[162]

In 1984 we acquired solid experimental evidence that new brain cells replace dying cells all the time. Macrophages remove the old debris of discarded brain cells, and an army of astrocytes burst and release special nerve growth factors to replace them with new cells and connections. God's creative power is at work! In Bible language, "all things are become new!" Such research brings a more profound understanding of the Bible promises just related. Furthermore, these evidences cancel the earlier notion of brain scientists that once a brain cell dies it is never replaced.

What about the sense of the awfulness of wrongdoing when we confess it to the Highest Power? In the presence of that Highest Power, our sense of His purity intensifies our abhorrence for any sins that have plagued us. Furthermore, we become overwhelmingly grateful for His grace. His grace is twofold: merciful forgiveness and overcoming power![163] Together, these two experiences gained from our confession to Him make the difference.

Even if you are suffering from heavy emotional turmoil and dysfunction, and you do not know why, you do not need to dig into the past. *You do not need to resurrect any buried and forgotten painful experiences.* **You need only to deal with the present pain and**

dysfunction. And the best treatment is the treatment of God's grace direct from the God of matchless love! **The most effective counselors cannot heal.** They can only lead their clients through the steps that will bring them to the One who does the healing. That One actually draws the client to Himself during the counseling session. Effective counselors will proceed with dialogue and sensitivity. They identify that what the client really wants is the *healing* of the dysfunction. As they work out a plan jointly with the client, they include the greatest plan for freedom from painful memories, —the story of Calvary. They step their client through the simple steps of coming to Christ:

1. acknowledging His sacred character,
2. presenting their need,
3. confessing their sin (not specified in the hearing of the human counselor)
4. acknowledging their unworthiness,
5. acclaiming His authority and power and forgiveness.

The plan might include reflecting or meditating upon, and visualizing the accounts in all four Gospels. For clients unfamiliar with the background account of events leading to Calvary, an abbreviated briefing could be helpful. This might include the Bible account of

- Lucifer's fall, and name change to Satan,
- The entrance of sin in the human race,
- Our genetic nature to sin,
- How God the Son was born in human flesh,

- How He understands our trials and human struggles,
- How He taught us by precept and example *the way* to overcome sin in human flesh,
- His experience of our pain, and our dying,
- His supreme redemptive price on Calvary,
- His glorious resurrection and ascension to heaven,
- His promise to return to resurrect and take to heaven all those who have accepted Him as their Redeemer and Lord.

Counselors need not feel that they must secure the client's decision to accept Christ. Counselors can answer any questions the client has, clarify anything the client wishes clarified, determine the client's wishes, and encourage the client to follow through on their convictions. I have found it helpful to clients if they know that any desire they find in their hearts to accept Christ, as their personal Savior *is evidence* that God loves them and is drawing them. *None of us can feel sorry for our sins unless God brings us the spirit of repentance.*[164]

POSTULATE 40: Forgiving and being forgiven heals.

A lot of people have a hard time forgiving. They lick their wounds, and secretly hope the other person will learn a lesson! But in the process, their harboring of the memory of how they were wronged is taking its toll. Their immune system is losing its fighting power. In addition, the resentful spirit is building up. And the critical spirit. And the defensive spirit. But when you forgive, all of that is changed. And healing begins.

When our Savior taught us to pray "Forgive us our debts as we forgive our debtors", He was teaching that it is in harmony with His law to bless us with the same blessing we impart to others. We enjoy a deep sense of joy and peace when we forgive others. And others experience that joy and peace when they know in their hearts that you have forgiven them.

This law of heaven is written in our brain and in our body. When we forgive, our immune system is turned on to further bless us. When others feel forgiven, their immune system is turned on. Both the giver and the receiver of forgiveness are blessed. Forgiving and being forgiven is healing.

In the synagogue on the Sabbath, Jesus referred to an Old Testament prophecy concerning Himself and His work. He read:

"The Spirit of the Lord is upon Me,
Because He has anointed Me
To preach the gospel to the poor;

205

He has sent Me to heal the brokenhearted,
To proclaim liberty to the captives
And recovery of sight to the blind,
To set at liberty those who are oppressed;
To proclaim the acceptable year of the Lord."

Then He closed the book, and gave it back to the attendant and sat down. And the eyes of all who were in the synagogue were fixed on Him.

And He began to say to them, "Today this Scripture is fulfilled in your hearing."[165]

This was the work of Jesus when on this earth. This is the work He continues today through His Holy Comforter, also translated "Helper".[166] He is the Mighty Counselor[167] He is still the Great Physician. He who flung the worlds into existence by His spoken word, He, who healed whole villages of people when He walked on earth, is healing today by His creative power. He is healing the broken brain.

Conclusion

To see broken hearts mended, families finding the fun of living, new goals achieved, barriers to growth and fulfillment tumbling down, new directions to new horizons--these are only a few of the exciting rewards that come from implementing the principles of true healing.

We have offered only a sampling of major principles and tested postulates that undergird the healing process. Our purpose has been to encourage all of us to build upon the sound principles that have been shown to contribute to true growth and psychological health.

My personal conviction is that while theory can be useful in providing structural guidelines, the true scientist never operates on the assumption that the theory is true! Every confirmed scientist knows that a theory is to provide the stimulation for the development of hypotheses that can be tested. Furthermore, good testing must meet rigorous standards of sample selection and controlled testing. After these standards have been rigorously followed, the scientist observes his findings in terms of "probabilities", never in terms of absolute truth!

Furthermore, global theories for counseling often ignore important **values** that have stood the test of time, and have promoted true healing for the individual and for society. Such time-tested values, tested across all cultures for more than four thousand years are those found in the Bible, God's written word to mankind.

These values are too often unwittingly sacrificed for the preservation of theories. In treating the broken brain, too often long-term outcomes have been ignored for immediate but very temporary satisfactions. By mastering the principles underlying psychological growth, these principles will leap into consciousness when we need them. We can use these principles to check whatever counsel we receive. With these principles to guide us, we can make our journey toward healing safely, in peace and in the fullness of joy!

References and End-Notes

[1] Bergland, Richard. *The Fabric of the Mind.* N.Y.: Viking Penguin Inc., 1985-6. 149-150.

[2] In the Bible book of *Isaiah,* chapter 26, verse 3 and the book of *Acts,* chapter 17, verse 28.

[3] In the Bible book of *Proverbs,* chapter 23, verse 7.

[4] Eccles, J. C., 'The Effects of Nerve Cross-union on Muscle Contraction', in *Exploratory Concepts in Muscular Dystrophy,* Excerpta Medica, Amsterdam, 1966. [Eccles gives the first description of genes 'switching on' in response to commands from the brain.] A technique called 'hybridization histochemistry' devised by John Coghlan in 1984 has enabled scientists to see a switched on gene and better understand the brain's ability to regulate the genes. First described in Coghlan, J., *et al,* Hybridization Histochemistry: Use of Recombinant DNA for tissue Localization of Specific Messenger RNA Populations', *Clinical and Experimental Hypertension; Theory and Practice,* 6, 63-78, 1984.

[5] It is easy for scientists to misinterpret their findings. The hallmark of good science is the replication of those findings in a number of independent studies, — the more such replications the more certain they can be of their interpretations. Likewise, it is easy for Bible scholars to misinterpret Bible passages. Just one example of this is the dominant Church's early **misinterpretation** of a single Bible passage referring this Earth's relationship to the Universe. As a result, not only was Galileo forced to his knees to recant his published observations of the stellar heavens, but also scientific progress was seriously delayed. The Church had erroneously concluded that the earth was stationary and was the center of the universe. If the Church had studied *all* the Bible passages on the subject, they would have found that the Bible teaches what good science was finding to be true. The *principle of replication* applies to both good science and good Bible interpretation. Only good Bible interpretation can be acceptable as *divine revelation.*

[6] *The Great Ideas Today* (Chicago: Encyclopaedia Britannica, Inc., 1968), pp. 141, 143.

[7] White, *Education* (Mountain View, CA: Pacific Press Publishing Association, 1903), p. 17. (Note: Throughout this book, unless clearly referring to a particular person, the term "men" applies equally to "women", as are also the masculine pronouns. The

terms are used "generically" referring to any member or members of the human family).

[8] Eccles, John C., *Evolution of the Brain: Creation of the Self,* p. 237 (Routledge 1991).

[9] John C.Eccles, *How the Self Controls Its Brain, p. 180, 181* N.Y.,Berlin, Heidelberg:.Springer-Verlag, 1994.

[10] Sherrington, C. S. (1940) *Man on His Nature* (Cambridge University Press, London). (Second edition 1951.)

[11] *Complex Systems: Operational Approaches in Neurobiology, Physics and Computers,* edited by H. Haken (Springer, Berlin, Heidelberg 1986); also *Proc. Roy. Soc. London* **227,** 411-428 (1987) and Eccles, John C. *How the Self Controls Its Brain.* Berlin Heidelberg New York: Springer-Verlag 1994.

[12] Eccles, J. C. (1994) *How the Self Controls its Brain.* N.Y: Springer. Chapter 8.

[13] Libet, B. (1990) Cerebral processes that distinguish conscious experience from unconscious mental functions, in *The Principles of Design and Operation of the Brain,* edited by J. C. Eccles and O. D. Creutzfeldt (Experimental Brain Research, Series 21) (Springer, Berlin, Heidelberg), pp. 185-205, and General Discussion, pp. 207-211.

[14] Eccles, John C. *How the Self Controls the Brain.* N.Y.: Springer, 1994, p. 174, 175.

[15] Bible book of 2 *Corinthians,* chapter 10, verse 5.

[16] Bible book of 2 *Corinthians,* chapter 10, verse 4.

[17] Eccles, John C. *How the Self Controls the Brain.* Springe*r,* 1994, p. 180.

[18] Bible book of 2 *Corinthians,* chapter 10, verses 4, and 5.

[19] Bible book of *Revelation,* chapter 12, verses 7-9, and *Isaiah,* chapter 14, verse 12-15.

[20] B. F. Skinner was an influential behavioral psychologist who did his initial work with pigeons and observed that their behavior was easily shaped by providing them with appropriate rewards. He extended his studies to humans, especially children in the school environment. Skinner developed a model he called "Operant Conditioning" and adapted it for the development of "Programmed Learning". Widespread objection came from the Humanistic psychologists and from others who saw his theory as denying humans the free exercise of their will.

[21] Bible book of *Romans,* chapter 12, verse 21.

[22] Bible book of *Psalms,* Psalm 103, verse 2.

[23] Bible book of *Psalms,* Psalm 34, verse 7.

[24] White, Ellen G. *Ministry of Healing,* p. 251.

[25] Sadler, Wm. *Practice of Psychiatry,* Chapter 69.

[26] Ellen White, *Testimonies,* Vol. 5, page 513.

[27] Ellen White, *Ministry of Healing,* page 176.

[28] Ellen White, *Counsels on Health,* page 79.

[29] Ellen White, *Testimonies,* Vol. 2, p. 524.

[30] Ellen White, *Testimonies,* Vol. 1, p. 387

[31] Ellen White, *Ministry of Healing,* p. 246.

[32] William S. Sadler, *Practice of Psychiatry,* p. 969

[33] William S. Sadler, *Practice of Psychiatry,* p. 949.

[34] Ellen White, *Child Guidance,* pp. 199, 200.

[35] GABA is Gamma-amino-butyric acid, one inhibiting chemical in the central nervous system (brain and spine) of humans. The other inhibiting chemical in the central nervous system is Cystine. Both are amino acids and either one inhibits (puts the brakes on) the nerve cell it contacts.

[36] James, William. *Great Books of the Western World,* vol. 53, p. 83..

[37] White, Ellen G., *Testimonies,* vol. 4, p. 452.

[38] Ibid. *Steps to Christ,* p. 58.

[39] In the Bible book of *Ephesians,* chapter 2, verses 3 and 2.

[40] Those networks in the nervous system that operate without conscious choice, e.g. those controlling heart-beat.

[41] J.C. Eccles. *The Understanding of the Brain.* N.Y.:McGraw-Hill, 1973, page 77.

[42] *Op.cit.* chapter 3.

[43] In the Bible book of *Ecclesiastes,* chapter 9, verse 10.

[44] In the Bible book of *Romans,* chapter 2, verse 21.

[45] In the Bible book of *James,* chapter 1, verses 6-8.

[46] In the Bible book of *Mark,* chapter 9, verses 17-24.

[47] In the Bible book of *Galatians,* chapter 5, verses 22 & 23.

[48] These are a few of the expressions of Job during the times he was overcome with depression. They are found in the following order in the book of *Job,* chapter 10, verse 18; chapter 16, verses 12, 13, and 15; chapter 16, verse 6; were killed. Shortly after, his children and their houses were destroyed by a "great wind".After all of this his wife was adding to his stress load by telling him to curse God whom Job had served so faithfully. In fact,

God had declared Job to be blameless and upright, one who fears God and turns away from evil. Satan was insisting that Job's faithfulness was only because God had blessed him and prospered him.(Job 1:8-10)

The rest of the story gives us some reassuring insights. We learn who the real author of the troubles that come to this world. We learn that Satan is the author of the troubles that come to God's faithful. We learn of our own vulnerability under stress. We learn of God's mercy, grace, forgiveness, made available to us. We learn that ultimately God will overrule. We learn that God is the ultimate Sovereign in this world. We can find some answers to our questions that we begin with "Why...why... does this happen to me? The book of Job needs to be studied prayerfully by all of us in these days of mounting stress."

[49] In the Bible book of *Philippians*, chapter 4, verse 13 (New King James Version)

[50] In the Bible book of *Ecclesiastes*, chapter 9, verse 10.

[51] In the Bible book of *James*, chapter 1, verses 2-4.

[52] In the Bible book of *1 Corinthians,* chapter 15, verse 57.

[53] Goleman, Daniel. *Emotional Intelligence.* New York:Bantam Books, 1995; Bergland, Richard. *The Fabric of Mind,* N.Y.:Viking Penguin Inc. 1985; Achterberg & Lawlis, *Bridges of the Bodymind.*Champaign, IL:Institute for Personality & Ability Testing, 1980. Sadler, Wm. *The Practice of Psychiatry,* St. Louis:C.V. Mosby, 1953. pp. 1006-1013, 1019, 1020.

[54] In the Bible, in the *Second Book of Corinthians,* Chapter 3, verse 18. This statement was recorded in A.D. 60.

[55] In the Bible, in the book of *Proverbs,* Chapter 23, verse 7. This statement was recorded in 1000 B.C.

[56] In the Bible, in the book of *Matthew,* Chapter 12, verse 37. The context of these words of Jesus reveals two facts supported by controlled experimental studies: (1) Our words reflect and reveal our deep-seated thoughts and feelings. Sigmund Freud even extended this to the "slip of the tongue"; (2) Our words make a feed-back loop to brain and body centers that prompted them, compounding our deep-seated thoughts and feelings. Thus, our character and hence predispositions are strengthened for better or for worse!

[57] This feedback loop phenomenon is reported in laboratory control studies with and without the use of *curare* injections to control the feedback flow of neural energy from remote areas of muscle activity.

[58] "Metabolism" refers to all of the processes going on inside of us that are involved in the building up or destruction of body tissue. Digestion, assimilation, and excretion or removal of wastes are examples.

[59] A psychiatrist has a medical degree and specializes in treating disorders of the mind.

[60] The term "wholeness" in this book refers to the harmonious interaction of brain and body mechanisms.

[61] The term "complete restoration" in this book refers to the correction or removal of all destructive elements in brain and body . This would include destructive bacteria, viruses, chemicals, destructive imbalances of brain and body interactions.

[62] **Interneuron** A nerve cell that is neither purely sensory nor motor but connects other neurons. In so doing,

unwanted events (thoughts, emotions, or actions) are inhibited or prevented from happening.

[63] In the Bible book of *Psalms* chapter 139 verse 14. In the verses before and after, David reflects on how wonderfully we are made, and how all of our body faculties were envisioned by the Creator according to a profound plan.

[64] Achterberg & Lawlis, *Bridges of the Bodymind.*Champaign, IL:Institute for Personality & Ability Testing, 1980.

[65] Borysenko, Joan. *Minding the Body, Mending the Mind.*.Reading, Mass. Addison-Wesley Publishing Company, Inc. 1987.

[66] See Wenzlaff, Richard "The Mental Control of Depression," in Wegner and Pennebaker, *Handbook of Mental Control.*

[67] Beck, Aaron. *Love is Never Enough.* New York: Haper and Row, 1988, pp. 145-146.

[68] In the Bible book of *Matthew,* chapter 9, verse 6.

[69] In the Bible book of *Hebrews,* chapter 11, verse 1.

[70] Bible book of *Romans,* chapter 10, verse 17.

[71] Bible, in the book of *1 John, chapter 5, verse 18. (New King James Version)*

[72] Bible, in the book of *1 Corinthians, chapter 13, verses 4 through 7.(New King James Version)*

[73] Bible, in the book of *Philippians,* chapter 3, verse 13.

[74] Bible, in the book of *Galatians, chapter 6, verse 7.* Put simply, the verse says 'we reap what we sow'.

[75] White, E.G. *Steps to Christ, pp.57, 58.* The reference reads as follows:
"The character is revealed, not by occasional good deeds and occasional misdeeds, but by the tendency of the habitual words and acts."

[76] Bible, in the book of *Matthew, chapter 26, verse 41.* See also *Psalm 103, verse 12-14, 17.*

[77] Bible, in the book of *Proverbs, chapter 24, verse 16. (New King James Version)*

[78] Bible, in the book of *John, chapter 3, verse 17.*

[79] The Bible book of *Isaiah, chapter 14, verses 12-20.* In the New King James version, these verses read:
"How you are fallen from heaven,
O Lucifer, son of the morning!

How you are cut down to the ground,
You who weakened the nations!
For you have said in your heart:
I will ascend into heaven,
I will exalt my throne above the stars of God;
I will also sit on the mount of the congregation
On the farthest sides of the north;
I will ascend above the heights of the clouds,
I will be like the Most High,
Yet you shall be brought down to Sheol,
To the lowest depths of the Pit.
Those who see you will gaze at you,
And consider you, *saying:*
'Is this the man who made the earth tremble,
Who shook kingdoms,
Who made the world as a wilderness
And destroyed its cities,
Who did not open the house of his prisoners?'

"All the kings of the nations,
All of them, sleep in glory,
Everyone in his own house;
But you are cast out of your grave
Like an abominable branch,
Like the garment of those who are slain,
Thrust through with a sword,
Who go down to the stones of the pit,
Like a corpse trodden underfoot,
You will not be joined with them in burial,
Because you have destroyed your land
And slain your people.
The brood of evildoers shall never be named."

[80] The Bible book of *Acts,* chapter 17, verse 28; also the book of *Colossians,* chapter 1, verse 17.

[81] The Bible book of *Galatians,* chapter 5, verses 16-23.

[82] Bible book of *Galatians,* chapter 6, verses 7 and 8.

[83] Cattell, Raymond, et al. *16 PF.* Champaign, Ill.: Institute for Personality and Ability Testing.

[84] Sweney, Arthur B. et al. *MAT.* Champaign, Ill.: Institute for Personality and Ability Testing.

[85] An expression in The Bible, in the book of *Isaiah,* Chapter 57, verses 20, 21. These particular verses declare that those who experience such inner turmoil are violating laws of which they are fully aware. Such symptoms of unrest and instability suggest that there may be underlying concerns with one's own values. People need to examine themselves in this regard.

[86] Cattell, R. B. & Gorsuch, R. L. The definition and measurement of national morale and morality. *Journal of Social Psychology,* 1965, 67, 77-96.

[87] The Bible book of *Isaiah,* Chapter 57, verse 20. All sickness and pain, all suffering and sorrow, are the results of law transgressed. The wonderful human machinery has been tampered with, and its delicate mechanism has been made to run counter to the law of its life and persistency; disease and death are the result.

[88] In the Bible book of *1 John, Chapter 3, verse 4.*

[89] Adapted from the publishers' preface to White, E. G. *Ministry of Healing,* Pacific Press Publishing Association, 1909.

[90] The Bible book of *Jude* verses 22 and 23.

[91] White, E. G. *Education,* Mt. View, CA: Pacific Press Publishing Association, 1903, page 29.

[92] The Bible book of *Mark,* chapter 2, verse 7-11; *Psalm 103,* verse 3.

[93] The Bible book of *Psalms,* Psalm 51, verses 10, 11.

[94] The Bible book of *First Corinthians,* chapter 10, verse 13.

[95] *Proverbs,* chapter 15, verse 1.

[96] *Proverbs,* chapter 16, verse 24.

[97] *Proverbs,* chapter 21, verse 2: "Every way of a man is right in his own eyes." Also *Proverbs,* chapter 16, verse 2: "All the ways of a man are clean in his own eyes;."

[98] *Proverbs,* chapter 16, verse 7.

[99] The Bible book of *First John,* Chapter 3, verse 4.

[100] The Bible book of *Isaiah* Chapter 1 verses 5 and 6 (New King James Version)

[101] The Bible book of *Psalms* Chapter 103 verse 3.

[102] The Bible book of *Isaiah* Chapter 58 verse 1.

[103] The Bible book of *Isaiah,* Chapter 40, verses 1 and 2, New King James Version.

[104] The Bible book of *John* Chapter 16, verse 12. These were the words of Jesus to his disciples.

215

[105] The literal meaning of the Greek word from which it is derived is variously given as "temperate" or "self-controlled". This is the word used in the Bible book of *1 Corinthians,* chapter 9, verse 25. In this reference the figure of speech used is drawn from athletes, who in preparing themselves for the games abstained from unwholesome food, wine, and sexual indulgence. Today's athletes preparing for the Olympics likewise exercise the same kind of self-control by abstaining from certain foods and practices that would hinder them from achieving their best performance. Aside from helping them increase their endurance and physical strength, such self-control has proved necessary to assure them of endurance and strength of mental concentration and focused attention. Mind and body intimacy is here again brought into focus.

[106] Bible book of *Galatians,* chapter 6, verse 7. *New King James Version.*

[107] Many of these possibilities are suggested by Richard Bergland in his fascinating book, *The Fabric of the Mind,* 1985, Viking.

[108] Davis, C. M. Self-selection of diet by newly weaned infants. *American Journal of Diseases of Children,* 1928, 36, 651-679),

[109] Richter, C., and Eckert, J.F. Mineral metabolism of adrenalectomized rats studied by the appetite method. *Endocrinology,* 1938, 22, 214-224.

[110] Chalmers, Elden M. Unpublished study done at the University of Tennessee, 1967.

[111] Wilkins, L. and Richter, C. P. A great craving for salt by a child with cortico-adrenal insufficiency. *Journal of the American Medical Association,* 1940, 114, 866-868.

[112] Bible book of *Matthew,* chapter 25, verses 14 to 30. Here Jesus relates a parable of the talents. He reveals that a person's moral character is definitely related to his multiplication of talents.

[113] White, E.G. *Education,* Mt. View, CA: Pacific Publishing Assn, 1903, p. 29.

[114] Kegan, R. G. (1986) . The child behind the mask: Sociopathy as developmental delay. In W. W. Reid, D. Dorr, J. I. Walker, & J. W. Benner III (Eds.), *Unmasking the psychopath* (pp. 45-77), New York: W. W. Norton.]

[115] Magid, Ken & McKelvey, Carole A. (1987). *High Risk, Children Without A Conscience,* New York: Bantam Books. 1989

[116] The Bible book of *John* Chapter 4, verses 17 and 18.

[117] The Bible book of *Romans* Chapter 1, verse 19, 20.

[118] In the Bible book of Matthew, Chapter 11, verse 28.

[119] The Bible book of *John,* Chapter 15, verse 5. Jesus Himself declared this.

[120] Bible book of *Matthew,* chapter 19, verse 26.

[121] Dorsey, John Morris. *The Foundations of Human Nature,* New York: Longmans, Green & Co., 1935. Dorsey was a practicing psychiatrist.

[122] Bietz, Arthur. I recorded these statements as they were made by Dr. Bietz.

[123] C.R. Snyder et al. "The Will and the Ways: Development and Validation of an Individual-Differences Measure of Hope," *Journal of Personality and Social Psychology 60, 4 (1991), p. 579*

[124] Cattell, R.B. et al. *Handbook for the 16PF,* 1970 edition.pp. 91,92

[125] Kagan, Jerome. *Galen's Prophecy,* New York: Basic Books, 1994, *pp. 155-170*

[126] Cattell, R. B. et al. *Handbook for the 16PF,* 1970 edition, pp. 91.92.

[127] These strategies are currently in preparation for publication in a companion volume to *Healing the Broken Brain.*

[128] Observations were done with Doreen Arcus and detailed in Kagan, Jerome. *Galen's Prophecy.*

[129] In the *Holy Bible,* New King James Version, *Isaiah,* Chapter 26, Verse 3.

[130] See Lawlis, G. Frank & Jean Achterberg. *Bridges of the Bodymind, 1980,* Champaign, Il:Institute for Personality and Ability Testing, Inc. c1980. See also.

[131] Frank, J. D. *Persuasion and Healing.* Baltimore and London: Johns Hopkins University Press, 1973.

[132] Sadler, William. *Practice of Psychiatry.* St. Louis: C.V. Mosby, c1953, p. 1012.

[133] In the *Holy Bible,* New King James Verson, the book of *Matthew,* Chapter 7, Verses 5-13 and in the book of *Luke* Chapter 7, Verses 1-10.

[134]In the *Holy Bible,* the book of *Acts,* Chapter 17, Verses 18, 24, and 28.

[135]Sadler, William. *Practice of Psychiatry.* St Louis:C.V. Mosby, c1953, p. 1013.

[136] In the Holy Bible, the book of *Romans,* Chapter 10, Verse 17.

[137] In the Holy Bible, the book of *Galatians* Chapter 5, Verses 20, and 21.

[138] In the Holy Bible, the book of *1 Corinthians,* Chapter 13, Verses 4 through 8.

[139] Borysenko, Joan. *Minding the Body, Mending the Mind.* Reading, Mass.: Addison-Wesley Publishing Company, Inc. 1987.

[140]The Bible book of *Psalms,* Psalm 103, verses 1 to 4.

[141] Two insightful and fascinating statements relating to the power of prayer to receive nerve ennervating energy from God are shared here: "Pray that the mighty energies of the Holy Spirit, with all their quickening, recuperative, and transforming power, may fall like an electric shock on the palsy-stricken soul, causing every nerve to thrill with new life, restoring the whole man from his dead, earthly sensual state to spiritual soundness." *White, E. G.* 5T267. Referring to the humanity of Jesus, the same author states: "As a man He supplicated the throne of God till His humanity was charged with a heavenly current that should connect humanity with divinity. Through continual communion He received life from God, that He might impart life to the world. His experience is to be ours." *Desire of Ages,* p. 363.

[142]The Bible books of *Philippians,* chapter 1, verse 6; *Psalms,* Psalm 138, verse 8; *Jude,* verse 24; *1 Corinthians,* chapter 15, verse 57. Each of these references assures us that God actively involves Himself to finish what He begins in each of us. The last reference assures us that God is able to keep us from falling back into our old ways. By studying each reference, each given by a different Bible author claiming Divine Authorship, and noting their agreement, we can be more certain that we are interpreting the references correctly.

[143] The Bible book of *John,* chapter 17, verse 15.

[144]Hormonal secretions are not the only determinants of sexual orientation. At least seven different factors have to be taken into account, according to Haeberle, E. J. (1978). *The Sex Atlas.* In this statement we are emphasizing the role of bonding

and hormonal secretions. The temper of the times suggests that to raise the question as to whether adult homosexual behavior should be regarded as normal or not is to convey narrow-minded prejudice or bigotry. However, both the Bible and modern science emphasize that the survival of the species requires heterosexual mating and consequential reproduction. See Stoller, R. J. (1976) *Perversion: the erotic form of hatred.* Hassocks, Sussex.
[145]The Bible book of *John,* chapter 3, verse 17.

[146]After fifty years of separation, when we recounted this experience my former room-mate tells me he recalls that it was "Ruskets" instead of "shredded wheat".
[147] Restak, Richard M. *The Mind,* New York: Bantam Books, 1988. pp. 41-44.
[148]Restak, op cit., p. 44.
[149]Restak, op cit. p. 94.
[150] Restak, op cit., p. 71.
[151]Carkhuff is a highly respected researcher in the field of counseling.
[152]The Bible book of *Proverbs,* chapter 21, verse 2.
[153] The Bible book of *Proverbs,* chapter 17, verse 22. (New King James Version)
[154] Benson, J. *The relaxation response.* New York: William Morrow, 1975.
[155]Achterberg & Lawliss. *Bridges of the Bodymind,* Champaign, Il: Institute for Personality and Ability Testing. 1980.
[156]Selye, Hans. *The Stress of Life.* New York: McGraw, 1956.
[157]Achterberg & Lawliss. *Bridges of the Bodymind,* op cit.

[158] The Bible book of *1 Peter* chapter 5, verse 7.
[159] The Bible book of *Matthew* chapter 11, verse 28.
[160]The Bible book of *1 Peter chapter 5 verses 6 and 7.*
[161]The Bible book of *2 Corinthians,* chapter 5, verse 17.
[162] The Bible book *Romans,* chapter 12, verse 1.
[163]The Bible book of *Hebrews,* chapter 4, verse 16.
[164] The Bible book of *John,* chapter 6, verse 44.
[165]The Bible book of *Luke,* chapter 4, verse 18-21.
[166]The Bible book of *John,* chapter 14, verse 16.(New King James Version)
[167]The Bible book of *Isaiah,* chapter 9, verse 6